Backyard
POULTRY
- *Naturally*

Third edition

Alanna Moore

PYTHON
PRESS

Python Press
PO Box 929 Castlemaine
Victoria 3450 Australia
pythonpress@gmail.com

ISBN - 9780975778289

First published February 1998
Second edition November 1998
Python Press edition 2004
Third edition March 2014

Designed by Joanne Marchese Design
Illustrated by Jenny Bullock
Cover photo: Alanna Moore

Thanks to Megg Miller for her invaluable assistance.

The opinions, advice and information contained in this publication have not
been provided at the request of any person but are offered solely for
information purposes. While the information contained in this publication has
been formulated in good faith, the contents do not take into account all the
factors that need to be considered before putting that information into
practice. Accordingly, no person should rely on anything contained herein as
a substitute for specific advice.

Contents

Why keep poultry?

Why not just buy eggs and takeaway chicken?

The eating of chicken meat and eggs used to be much more of a luxury than it is today. Since the 1950s consumption in Australia has risen over 150 fold.[1] With the rise of intensive factory farming, the special Sunday roast chicken has been replaced with mass-produced cheap cuts and takeaways that we all take for granted. But at what cost to the chicken, the consumer and the traditional farmer?

In 1996, representatives of a southern Indian farmers' organisation stormed the newly opened, Pepsi Cola-owned, Kentucky Fried Chicken (KFC) outlet in Bangalore. They demanded that the company pack up and leave India. In a country where more than 70% of the population depends on traditional agriculture for their livelihood, they feared that KFC's monoculture factories would jeopardise their own food security.[2]

Factory farming of fowl is a form of economic rationalism which creates unemployment and social disintegration. One person can 'care' for tens of thousands of fowl housed intensively in barns or batteries – after all, all they have to do is check feed and water containers and remove dead bodies. There are serious concerns about animal welfare.

Belsen for birds

Despite the work of animal welfare societies, poultry in factory farms (some 50 billion worldwide in 2009) are usually exempt from many provisions of freedom from cruelty legislation. Institutionalised cruelty has thus been 'legalised' and accepted as normal in our society.

The reality hidden inside the huge shed walls would be distressing for most consumers. Battery farm hens have to endure a year or so of overcrowded, stressful conditions. Batteries of cages are often stacked vertically, several cages high. The wire floors, with an uncomfortable 1 in 5 slope, often cripple the birds' feet and legs. On occasion, the

1

hens' toenails grow so long that they end up permanently tangled in the wire, leaving the bird unable to feed and doomed to die.[3]

Up to seven hens are crammed into cages so small that they can barely turn and certainly can't stretch out their wings, having typically less than the size of an A4 piece of paper each. Australia's twelve million battery hens live in enormous sheds of up to 50,000 birds in each.[4]

Denied room for natural behaviour, crowded battery hens become noisy and nervous. They are reluctant to lay eggs under crowded conditions and frantically seek privacy. Sometimes they will even lay in the dead body of another hen.

Hens don't have to be happy to lay eggs. Egg laying is a biological function determined by breeding, levels of dietary protein and light.

The hens' instinct to dustbathe is also strong. They try to bathe on wire floors, resulting in lost feathers and bare, raw skin. Sometimes the hens are kept in darkness for 24 hours without food or water in order to force them to moult, so that they will start to lay again quickly.

Boredom and stress from overcrowding in badly ventilated sheds, lack of access to feed, water shortage and irritation from lice infestation can all lead to disease, as well as feather picking and cannibalism.

Hens purchased from a battery farm. Note the lost feathers and bare skin.

The factory farmer's answer to these so-called vices is 'debeaking', a practice in which around a third of a chick's beak is removed, often very roughly. Debeaking is extremely painful. It damages the sensitive nerve layer, which is much like the quick of a human fingernail. Following debeaking birds eat less and lose weight because of the agonising pain, which may last for the rest of their lives. [5]

Egg farms often operate with hens dying at a rate of 10 - 15% annually from stress-related problems.[6] Hens commonly endure broken bones and painful fractures from over-production of eggs and lack of exercise. Prolapse and tumours are common, as is collapse from 'layer fatigue'. The hens' productive lives last a mere eighteen months, after which they are considered spent and are disposed of.

Commercial chicken feed may contain all manner of nasties including genetically modified soya beans. [7] Chicken meat and eggs often harbour residues of antibiotics that were added to feed to foster growth. This is thought to be a major cause of antibiotic resistant 'super bugs' in humans, a serious issue for public health. [8]

Arsenic-based drugs were approved by America's FDA for use in animal feed - to make chickens grow quicker and make meat look pinker (i.e. 'fresher') - right up until October 2013. Now banned there, this arsenic had turned up in rice crops fertilised with poultry manure. Arsenic has never been allowed in the EU. [9] Hormones are generally not allowed as feed additives (only because they are not effective growth promoters).

Another problem may come from flooring or deep litter woodchips. A highly toxic carcinogen, the wood preservative PCP has been detected in fowl (and their eggs) that have been reared on wood shavings.

On the welfare front, the European Union ended a twelve year phase-out of barren battery cages in January 2012. Replacement with 'enriched' cages and other systems is now complete in the UK, but fourteen other member nations were still not compliant 1 year later. [10] While Switzerland banned battery cages way back in 1992, I'm told that customers still prefer to buy the cheaper battery cage eggs imported from South America. So they have merely exported the problem.

In the USA, the state of California is phasing out battery cages by 2015 and Michigan has also committed to a phase out by 2019. [11]

Broilers are no better off

Fowl that are raised for meat are usually a pitiful lot. Selectively bred for their super fast growth rate and enormous size, their small, weak legs are barely able to carry them. Not bred for hardiness or disease resistance, like the layers, they must be fed chemical additives and antibiotics to keep them alive and growing fast on the factory farms.

Kept in groups of over 40,000, broilers are packed into huge darkened sheds at a density of about 20 birds per square metre. Barely able to move in the shed, the bloated baby birds often suffer severe leg problems, heart attacks, fatty livers and kidneys, as well as disease. Feather pecking and cannibalism is rife.

At 5 - 7 weeks of age, if they have survived that long, the broilers are sent off to be slaughtered. Such was the fate of nearly half a billion fowl in Australia in 2014 (up from 3 million in 1950).[12]

Free-range poultry

Now if you thought that free-range eggs were produced under natural conditions – it ' ain' t necessarily so' ! Free-range farm hens may not have year-round access to green pick and may still be fed and medicated the same dangerous inputs as factory fowl.

Free-range hens may also suffer stress from unnaturally over-crowded conditions. Australian states still have no proper regulations and dither about whether to increase the number of free-range hens from a recommended 1,500 to the hectare to 20,000 or more, the latter being a stocking rate on some 80% of so-called free-range farms. In huge flocks there is a lot of fighting and bullying. Shy birds miss out at feeding time.

And wherever free-range guidelines are only voluntary, unscrupulous producers will try to sell battery eggs as free-range. So if you don' t know the supplier and want to ensure good welfare, then only eggs labelled as " organically certified" or " pastured eggs" might be trusted.

As for the Royal Society for the Prevention of Cruelty to Animals accredited 'barn eggs' branding, flocks enjoy limited freedom in a controlled barn environment, at 7 to 9 birds per m². [13] Better than a battery, birds may still be stressed. Debeaking is also not outlawed by Australia's RSPCA; an organization, I was told by an ex-inspector, that has been "totally infiltrated by the chicken industry".

The full value of poultry

Poultry are multi-functional micro-livestock. They are lovely, useful pets that add colour and entertaining antics to the backyard, providing a non-stop spectacle. Each individual character goes about its life – foraging industriously, dustbathing blissfully, preening and scratching. It is so relaxing to watch and interact with poultry. In fact - it's an excellent anti-stress therapy!

Children can learn and enjoy much from raising chickens and ducklings. Some adult birds can even be classed as cuddly – the Silkie in particular. Regular contact with birds ensures their friendliness. However, friendliness can lead to cheekiness, so keep the doors shut and feed bins closed, and mind they don't trip you up at feed time!

Feeding the 'chooks', a relaxing task.

5

Your feathered friends will also lay nutritious eggs for you. These will have a better nutritional status than battery eggs, including higher levels of vitamin B[12]. And artificial colouring agents will not be needed to improve yolk colour, if the hens can forage on greens. [14]

Backyard poultry can work tirelessly as gardeners, lawn mowers, scrap disposalists, organic pest and weed controllers and security guards. You might even get to eat the odd unwanted bird, especially at cockerel or drake removal time, when those once adorable chicks start crowing competitions in the middle of the night and the drakelings start to harass ducks. Home-grown meat is definitely the tastiest!

In some cultures preparations of fowl meat are regarded not only as a delicacy, but also as medicine. The Chinese drink a broth made from breast meat to strengthen the lungs. This is similar to that age-old European remedy, the cure-all - Chicken Soup.

Have I convinced you to keep poultry naturally? I hope so!

Endnotes

[1] http://www.animalsaustralia.org/factsheets/broiler_chickens

[2] Fanton, J. & Fanton, M. 1996 'KRRS vs KFC', *The Seed Savers' Network Newsletter*, no. 20, Autumn, p. 6.

[3] Singer, P. 1975, *Animal Liberation*, Granada/Paladin, United Kingdom, p. 113.

[4] Australian Egg Corporation 2013

[5] Animal Liberation, n.d. *Battery Hens* (leaflet), Animal Liberation, Australia.

[6] Singer, P. 1975, *Animal Liberation*, Granada/Paladin, United Kingdom, p. 117.

[7] https://www.steggles.com.au/chickens

[8] *How drugs pumped into supermarket chickens pose a terrifying threat to our health* Daily Mail (UK) 10/8/2013 (online).

[9] *F.D.A. Bans Three Arsenic Drugs Used in Poultry and Pig Feeds*, New York Times, 1/10/13 (online).

[10] http://www.ciwf.org.uk/farm_animals/poultry/egg_laying_hens/

[11] http://www.voiceless.org.au/the-issues/battery-hens

[12] Davis, K. 1996, *Prisoned Chickens, Poisoned Eggs: an inside look at the modern poultry industry*, Phd Book Publishing Company, United States of America. http://www.animalsaustralia.org/factsheets/broiler_chickens.php

[13] http://www.rspca.org.au/shophumane/farming-facts/layer-hens/layer-hens-lifecycle/

[14] http://articles.mercola.com/sites/articles/archive/2011/09/02/why-does-this-commonly-vilified-food-actually-prevent-heart-disease-and-cancer.aspx

Poultry Behaviour and Management

Poultry behaviour

Fowl behaviour
In their natural environment fowl live in tropical jungles, in family groups of a dozen or so birds. The original Jungle fowl *(Gallus gallus)* is still found wild in Asian and Pacific forests. From this bird hundreds of domesticated varieties have been bred, most of which look totally different from their common ancestor. Naked-necked fowl are also found wild in Asia; while in South America the Araucauna has characteristic ear tufts and lays blue- or green-shelled eggs.

Strongly territorial and creatures of habit, fowl always come home to roost each evening in the same spot. This makes them ideal livestock as they bond to your backyard and generally won' t stray. Although they are good flyers in the wild, this ability has been bred out of most modern poultry, along with other useful instinctual behaviour.

Fowl bond to your backyard and generally won't stray.

The social order of fowl

Fowl have a strong social hierarchy maintained by their pecking order, as each tries to dominate others in the flock. The leading bird will often scoff the best food, eat the most and may well be the best egg producer (but not always). Meeker birds will be bullied away from food so it is important to provide enough feed stations to make sure that everyone gets a feed.

Fowl easily learn to recognise a dozen or so other birds. After initial scuffles, harmony is quickly achieved in this optimum-size flock. By a system of raising and lowering heads to denote rank, the birds know where they stand on the social ladder.

In larger flocks the social order is much more complex and there is constant pecking and testing of social position. In flocks of over 100 individuals, especially, stress and aggression are the rule. With all the social tension they endure under commercial free-range conditions, hens in huge flocks could not be described as being contented.

Roosters and hens

Roosters are often thought of as noisy, unnecessary nuisances. In suburban areas they are often banned because of this. They can be aggressive when guarding their flock, even pecking the hand that feeds them. They can fight and kill competitors. And you certainly don' t need roosters for hens to lay eggs, only for breeding. In fact, some of them aren' t even good for breeding – if deprived of female company in their youth, they may later show no interest in hens.

Roosters have plenty of redeeming features, however. They improve the social cohesion of a flock and bring increased alertness and dashing beauty. They bravely guard hens and chickens, and tenderly summon their flock to devour any tasty morsels they' ve found. Roosters have lesser feed requirements than the hens, and may actually starve while watching over their feeding flock.

When hens go off the lay, the rooster soon loses interest in them. When the hens start to lay again he' ll try every trick under the sun to gain their attention.

Roosters improve the social cohesion of a flock.

When a hen is about to start laying, she informs the rooster, who struts around proudly with her, inspecting potential nest sites for suitability. This is accompanied by delightful chortlings as they go. After settling on the best nest site, the hen will test it out, shaping up materials around her and lining the nest with her downy breast feathers to wait for the arrival of the first egg.

All the while, an alert and anxious rooster will be pacing up and down, never far away. Some roosters crow with excitement at this point. When the hen triumphantly emerges from egg laying, she'll cluck with great celebration. The rooster and the rest of the family may join in the chorus, too.

The hen continues to lay her clutch at the chosen nest site, until she gets the urge to stay sitting on the eggs (goes 'broody' or 'clucky'). She then gets to have a rest from laying.

The size of the clutch each hen lays is genetically coded in her breeding. Silkies, for instance, are known for their excessive broodiness, and will start to sit after laying only 10 or 12 eggs. Araucanas, on the other hand, may not stop to sit until more than 80 eggs are laid.

The size of the eggs will depend on the size of the hen and the age at which the hen started to lay. Early maturing pullets lay very small eggs at first, but the eggs increase in size by the second year of laying.

The laying hen stands out from the rest physically. Her comb and wattles swell up plump and rich red – engorged with blood. Her vent becomes large and moist, her abdomen full and soft, and her pubic bones become flexible and more widely separated. When the hen goes off the lay, and also when she is sick, her comb and wattles become pale and limp.

Which hen is the best layer? She is the one that leaves first to go foraging in the morning and is the last to roost at night. She is the most active, chatty, friendly and alert, and is often the rooster's favourite. She may mature and lay early, lay during the moult, and/or into the winter.

Moulting

Each year, generally in summer or autumn, fowl start to moult and won't lay until their feathers grow back. Heat, stress or the lack of clean drinking water may trigger moulting at other times.

Hens that moult feather by feather while still laying the odd egg are the best layers. They have a quick, late moult of maybe 8 weeks in autumn, as opposed to a long summer moult of 12 to 16 weeks. As hens grow older they take longer to moult.

Preening

Birds oil their feathers when preening, by squeezing oil from the gland at the base of the tail with their beak and spreading the oil through their feathers. This helps to waterproof feathers and improve their appearance.

Dustbathing

Dustbathing is another important daily social ritual, which also helps rid birds of body lice and other parasites. Birds love to luxuriate in dry sandy baths, sunbathing together with wings outstretched.

Tales of the Aracaunas

I am forever amazed at the character traits of the Aracauna fowl. Not being domesticated for long, they are strong on instinct. I admire the sheer toughness of the breed: they'll camp by night in trees and thrive in rain, hail or shine, unlike many other breeds. Aracaunas are flighty, however, and for this reason may not always be best for the backyard.

Araucanas flirting.

I can only describe my Araucana roosters as absolute gentlemen and not ones to pick a fight, but then I could be biased. However, I had to admire the sheer ferocity of a friend's lavender rooster that I once minded. Cecil would attack any would-be handler, even in the dark of night. If I dared to remove his Silky cockerel pen mates he'd also take me on. He had his tender side, too. When a little chicken got separated from its family, Cecil adopted it and kept it warm at night.

Egbert, my first lavender rooster, was absolutely heroic. He would defend his chicks with his life, or nearly. He was just a bantam but it seems he took on a bird of prey, possibly the local wedge-tailed eagle. One winter's day he was found bleeding heavily, but his chicks were safe. We wrapped him up like a mummy, administered herbal healing cream and laid him by the fire. He was fine the next morning.

Some while after his brush with death Egbert disappeared, leaving a pile of lavender feathers behind. We thought that the eagle or a goshawk had probably carted him off. As he was our only rooster then, it was nice and quiet without his crowing. Then, one day about a week later, he appeared from out of the wilds as if nothing had happened. The boss of the fowl yard was back in business.

The Araucana's generally gentle nature, unfortunately, does not hold much sway in the love stakes. Hens are easily lured away by fiercer breeds. Jaffa, our small and slender Jungle Fowl rooster, is every hen's darling and, before his spurs were put to the grinder, he made a ferocious enemy. I made the mistake of keeping him and his harem in a yard adjoining my best Araucana rooster, Eggscalibur, and his

11

hens. There was plenty of taunting and showing off between the two roosters. Eventually Eggscalibur's hens could resist no longer and gradually all escaped into Jaffa's yard, refusing to return.

With none of his hens left, Eggscalibur moped and sank into deep depression for a day or two. Finally he could bear it no longer. Deciding to take a stand, he went on a fatal suicide mission into Jaffa's yard. Despite his bigger size he was mortally wounded and, by the time I rescued him the next morning, he was dying. I tried to revive him, but to no avail. You might say he died of a broken heart.

When I bought my first Aracaunas, a point-of-lay trio, their extreme nervousness, flightiness and secretiveness struck me. Having incubated and hand reared many dozens of these birds since then, I have been able to get to know their admirable qualities. The hand-raised birds being much quieter, more co-operative and charming.

Duck behaviour

Ducks don't have a pecking order like that of fowls. They are gregarious and friendly, although fairly highly strung and not usually appreciative of close human contact.

Most duck breeds originated from wild Asian waterfowl, the common ancestor being the Mallard *(Anas boschas)*. An exception is the

Muscovy ducks.

Muscovy *(Cairina moschata)*, a large duck species from South America. In the wild, ducks are strong fliers and move around in pairs.

Drakes are not 'drama queens' like roosters. They are quieter than the ducks and will only fight each other if ducks are around. Like roosters, they are the most colourful of the sexes. You can even keep a gang of drakes together, as pets and gardeners.

Egg-laying ducks can lay several hundred delicious eggs each year. In competitions held in the 1930s, ducks even out-laid hens. In terms of quantity, duck eggs are the world's most commonly eaten egg.

Two-thirds of the world's ducks are kept in China and South-East Asia, where they are employed to clean up paddy fields and control pests in crops. They are often trained as ducklings to stay near a flag placed where they are meant to forage.

Poultry management

Establishing the flock

When shopping for new poultry, you should always choose birds that are bright and active. Never choose birds that are hunched up, huddled or fluffed out. These birds are probably sick. Likewise, avoid birds with thick scaly legs; these are the legs of an old bird. Young birds' legs are fine and shiny.

The average family shouldn't need more than six hens or ducks to produce sufficient eggs. If you're starting off with chicks, you'll need to purchase a dozen or more, unless they're sexed, to make up for cockerel culls and mortalities in rearing.

If you decide to get point-of-lay hens, you will need to have a predator-proof night house and a run, or yard, waiting in readiness (see Chapter 4, 'Housing Backyard Poultry'). Night perches should be sturdy and rounded; branches, dowl or broom handles are all suitable. Quiet spots for nesting are also needed – about one nest for every five hens. A 20L bucket makes a great nest; just cut the lid down to about one-third to allow the hens access while keeping the nesting material inside. Keep new birds locked in the night house or pen for a week or so, to give them time to get over any trauma and to ' bond' to their new home and owner. They may not to be too impressed with you at first. Call out to them at feeding time, using the same call. This helps them recognise you.

If you get day-old chicks initially, you can keep them in a heated brooder made from large cardboard box. Later, when the chicks are about six weeks old and have feathered up, you could simply provide them with a mobile pen and build bigger quarters as they grow. Chicks will settle in a lot more quickly than older birds.

Never keep a bird on its own. Fowl are gregarious and will suffer great loneliness. Never introduce just one new bird at a time, either, as it will be bullied. Two new ones will cope better, especially if they are of the same age and size. Even better if they are the same breed. Birds prefer to socialise with their own breed.

Fowl are creatures of habit so you need to get a new flock settled quickly and establish your chosen routine from the start. Design well from the start. Don' t just dump them in a temporary spot for the first few days because they will bond strongly to that spot and keep going back there every night.

If you want your new flock to free range in a part of the garden, it is best to use the following method. Introduce them to their night house at dusk and actually place them up on perches to settle down. Lock up the night house and leave them in it for perhaps a week or more before allowing them out into wider territories.

Familiarise them with the free range by letting them out late in the afternoon at first, when there isn' t much time to get lost. Gradually increase time out by letting them out earlier each day. When they' ve settled in you can either let them out first thing after morning feed or in the late morning, after they have laid eggs. After that they will always come home to roost each evening.

Catching and moving birds

Catching poultry and moving them around isn' t much fun for the bird and you don' t really need the stress of running around fruitlessly in circles. You must understand their habits and work with them. If you need to catch them, do it at night, when they are quite dopey, or grab them at feed time when they are unsuspecting. Or you could herd them into a corner and take a dive.

Ducks can be herded more easily than fowl. Walk slowly behind them, with your arms outstretched, and wave in the direction you want them to walk. Never catch ducks by the legs as their legs are more prone to breaking than a fowl' s. It is better to grab ducks by the neck and then get a grip around the body. Hold them firmly, as you would a fowl, and make sure their posterior is pointed outwards – duck droppings are rather sloppy and messy!

Being transported to a new home can be very stressful for birds. Never put them in an airless bag or box, or in the boot of a car. Try to collect them on a cool day as heat can be a killer. A cardboard box with plenty of air holes or a birdcage is the preferred container for transportation.

Hold birds firmly around the body. Tuck them underarm to keep wings from flapping.

Management in temperature extremes

As fowl have no sweat glands, excess heat has to be eliminated via the lungs. When fowl are panting, with their mouths open, it means they are overheated.

In hot weather fowl eat less feed, therefore they need extra protein and concentrates. Heat puts a strain on birds, resulting in fewer, smaller eggs with poorer shells, and generally increased mortality.

It is vital to provide shady areas, using trees or shadecloth. In a heatwave you might spray yards and houses with a hose, and put ice blocks in the birds' water containers. Birds with heatstroke can be splashed with cool water.

Below 21°C fowl lose heat to the air and need to eat more to compensate. Keep their houses warm and draught free. Feed them extra grain, such as wheat, corn and barley. Corn and barley are warming foods. They should be fed in greater quantities in winter than in summer, when the ration should be minimal. See Chapter 5 for more detail.

An automatic waterer.

Leaving the flock unattended

Many people are wary of keeping backyard poultry because they feel it will tie them down too much: they feel that the need to feed the flock morning and night, and check little chickens several times daily is too much of a commitment.

However, with a good management system, that provides automatic feeders and waterers that rodents cannot access - you can go away for the weekend.

An automatic chicken feeder. Note the holes through which the feed pours into the feed tray.

Have a trustworthy mother hen or duck to take care of her own babes. Just make sure they have access to fresh water and crumble at all times, and are safely protected from predators.

It is a little more difficult to leave ducks unattended, simply because they foul up their water so regularly that they could get sick if you are not there to change their water. Even if you can devise a way to ensure fresh water is available at all times, feeding can also be a problem; you can't leave unlimited quantities of feed around because they will gorge themselves all at once.

If you want to keep ducks, you may need obliging neighbours or house sitters when you want to take a holiday.

Backyard Poultry Breeds

What type of backyard poultry would suit you best?

Ducks or fowl?
You should decide whether you wish to keep either ducks or fowl, as it is generally best not to have both in the same place at the same time. Ducks soon foul up the water and create unhygienic conditions for other poultry.

There are a number of factors you should consider when making your decision.

Is the garden a predominantly damp or dry environment? Ducks are hardier than fowl in damp conditions, where, in fact, they thrive.

Do you want to breed poultry, but local by-laws prohibit you from keeping a rooster? If this is the case, you can either import fertile eggs or choose ducks, which are quieter.

Are slugs or snails causing problems? These pests are hosts to tapeworm, to which fowl are vulnerable. It is better to employ ducks to eradicate them. Ducks are adept at this and forage better than fowl.

Do you find tall fences ugly? Ducks (except for ducks that fly, such as the Muscovy) are easily confined by fences low enough to step over.

Do you have small children? Ducks, being highly strung, hate to be harassed by children and do not enjoy being handled. A placid breed of fowl would make a cuddlier pet.

Ducks can be rather messy, fouling up their water with their wet droppings and eager dabbling. And, while they do not scratch in the garden, they will delve with their beaks and strip tasty plants bare. So ducks are better in a mulched area of the garden where tempting plants are protected.

As ducks sleep on the ground it is easy to house them – a shelter is all they need. Perches and nest boxes are not necessary. However, if confronted by a predator, ducks cannot fly to save themselves so they must be housed in secure surroundings.

Unfortunately there is often a stigma attached to eating duck eggs. Any worries are usually unfounded. As long as the eggs are laid in hygienic surroundings and collected promptly they are perfectly good to cook and eat. You can do anything with a duck egg that you can do with a fowl egg, although the slightly stronger taste may be best disguised by cooking them with other things.

A dam is not necessary for keeping ducks, but will be appreciated.

Laying, table or ornamental?
When choosing a poultry breed, keep in mind the purpose for which you intend to keep poultry.

In general, specific breeds are more suitable for one purpose than another. Australorps, for instance, are regarded as being good layers, while Indian Game are thought to be excellent ' table' , or eating, birds.

Ducks on a dam.

Frizzles, on the other hand, are renowned predominantly for their exotic looks.

A number of breeds – Faverolles, for instance – are described as being 'dual purpose'. This means that they are good eating birds as well as being good layers. Faverolles are also quite ornamental. Some breeds, such as Pekins, are better sitters and mothers than other breeds, too.

Some of the duck breeds, in particular, are good foragers and are particularly suited for inclusion in permaculture systems.

Standard or bantam?
Poultry comes in a range of sizes. 'Standard' and 'bantam' are the two main size groupings, although even within the range of standard birds there are variations in size. The Houdan is not a bantam but it is small in size compared to the Sussex and Orpington. Large, stocky standard breeds are described as being 'heavy'. Smaller birds are termed 'light'. Intermediate breeds such as the Welsummer are described as being 'medium' in size.

Some people are under the misconception that a bantam is a breed in itself. It isn't. The bantam is simply a smaller version of many fowl and duck breeds. Some bantam varieties, however, have no larger counterpart, the Japanese Bantam being one. These bantam breeds are called 'true bantams'.

Bantams were introduced to Europe by sea captains. 'Bantam' was actually the name of a port in Java where many tiny breeds were acquired by them.

Standard size birds eat a lot and lay medium to large eggs. Bantams lay smaller eggs, but their feed bill is dramatically less than that for standards.

Another advantage of bantams is that if local council regulations prohibit large fowl, it may be legal to keep bantams because they are classified as cage birds.

Heavy birds compact the ground, especially when they are overstocked or left too long in one area. When compacted, the soil becomes sour and lifeless because oxygen and water cannot infiltrate. Lightweight birds do not compact the ground as much.

Pure or crossbred?

Hybrid birds, or crossbreds, are often the best egg layers and the fastest growers. They may also be healthier than purebred fowl.

Unfortunately, factory farming has meant a reliance on a few highly bred types with limited genetic background. There are billions of identical white laying fowl bred purely for short-lived battery egg production.

If you are looking for consistency, hybrid birds are generally not worth breeding from because their genetic characteristics aren' t fixed, as they are with purebreds. Besides, crossbreds rarely go broody and are not known for their mothering ability.

Purebreds, bred from many years of judicious selection (and the odd mutation), were ' designed' to fill certain environmental niches in various parts of the world. There is a breed for every situation. And there are so many colours to choose from! Just as well, because in a natural situation a white bird would be easily spotted by a predator.

The increased popularity of crossbred birds has, unfortunately, seen the demise of many pure breeds.

I strongly encourage all backyard poultry keepers to maintain a rare pure breed of bird if they possibly can. This will prevent the looming threat of extinction of our priceless heritage. Think of it as being like heirloom seed saving. Who knows? One day the useful genes of such birds may be needed to breed up flocks of disease-resistant free-range fowl on a large scale.

I don' t recommend buying spent old battery hens – they are often highly in-bred cripples that need to be taught the ' ways of the wild' , such as how to perch. If you take pity on them, you are bolstering the battery egg industry by helping them dispose of ' waste products' .

Which sex?

I have already featured the good and bad points of roosters and drakes (Chapter 2), so when you have made a decision on which to keep, you may need to know how to tell the difference between the sexes.

Within the fowl fraternity the difference is usually fairly obvious; the rooster has the showier array of wattles, comb, tail and hackle feathers. However, in some breeds the cock displays ' hen feathering' . This makes sexing a little more difficult, at least until the age at which crowing starts. Cock-a-doodle-dooing, of course, is a dead giveaway.

Some people are able to sex day-old chickens. There are different clues according to the breed so it' s a very specialised skill. In many breeds the females feather up more quickly than the males, although the males' wattles develop more quickly and their feet will be larger. Males are more aggressive and will play at fighting together. Cockerels' tails are also more pointed than those of pullets, but it' s easy to be confused.

Some breeds of poultry are described as being ' auto-sexing' , meaning that the down colour of the hatchling chicks is distinctly different,

A Leghorn cockerel, just beginning to show signs that he is a he. Note the pointed tail and wattles that are slightly larger than those of a hen.

depending on the sex of the chick. Some special crossbred birds have been developed for this purpose. Each of these breeds' names end in 'bar', such as the Legbar (from the Leghorn), Dorbar (from the Dorking) and Cambar (from the Campine).

Sexing ducks can also be tricky, especially if the sexes have the same colouring. Mature drakes of many breeds have a telltale curled feather in their tail. Before maturity you can listen for the deeper quack of the drakeling, as opposed to the higher honking of the female.

Matching poultry with climate

When selecting birds, try to match them to your local climatic conditions. Fowl most suited to colder areas are the heavily feathered breeds such as Faverolles, Orpington and Silkie. Cold-climate ducks are large in size, with plenty of fat for insulation, the Rouen being a classic example.

For the other extreme, an excellent fowl for very hot conditions is the Transylvanian Naked Neck, which has up to 40% less feathering than normal fowl. If choosing heavily feathered birds in a hot climate, you will need to be able to provide plenty of shade or a cooling system.

Fowl for kids

Pekins, like Silkies, are calm and docile, and are the best fowl for kid's pets. Also good are Faverolles, Polish, Barnevelder and Dorkings.

Lucinda Cantrell and a Pekin rooster.

Breed profiles

Around the world, pure breeds of poultry that are our precious heritage are becoming ever rarer to obtain. Even seemingly commonplace varieties may be scarce.[1] The good old heritage breeds are well worth seeking out. (Bold numbers refer to breed photographs).

Fowl breeds

Ancona

A light Mediterranean breed, the highly ornamental Ancona has black feathers tipped with white. Anconas are hardy, active and economical to keep. They are good layers of white eggs. They mature rapidly, can be very flighty, and are not prone to broodiness.

Andalusion

The Andalusion is a light breed originating from Spain. It has blue feathers laced with black. Like other Mediterranean breeds, the Andalusion is very active, flighty and non-broody.

Aracauna

Aracauna have a different ancestry than most domestic breeds of fowl. Their ancestors originated in South America and were subsequently crossed with light breeds introduced by the Spanish. Descendents of the original Aracauna still sport tiny ' pea' combs and ' earrings' (tufts of feathers) that grow from a flesh pad adjacent to the ear lobe. Stock in Australia do not have ' earrings' as such, but ear muffs and beard are characteristic traits. All Aracauna lay coloured eggs, which range in colour from blue, green and turquoise to khaki. These ' Easter egg fowl' are very hardy, good foragers and excellent layers. Some are good broodies and mothers, too. Flightiness can be a problem. **19** and **22**.

Australorp

Australia' s own breed, the Australorp, is a large graceful bird clad in glossy black feathers, with a lustrous green sheen. It is a hardy, docile dual-purpose bird.

In 1992, an Australorp team won a world record for egg laying – six birds laid 1857 eggs in 365 days. Backyarders, however, should only expect to get about 250 light-brown eggs per year from well-cared-for Australorps.

A good all-rounder, the Australorp makes a good mother and is fairly broody. Male chicks display slower feathering than females from about 10 days to 2 months of age. **31**.

Barnevelder
This quiet Dutch breed is rich brown in colour. The Double Laced variety, in which each feather has two bands of darker brown, is the most popular.

A heavy breed of medium size, the Barnevelder is hardy, active and a reasonable layer of 120– 150 beautiful chocolate-brown eggs per year. Laying begins early in spring.

Barnevelders are placid and are easily confined. The roosters are protective but not aggressive. On the downside, the breed is somewhat susceptible to Marek' s disease (see Chapter 7). Chicks are shy and easily bullied by other breeds, especially at feed time. **33**.

Belgian bantams: Barbu d'Anvers, d'Uccle, Watermael
Quaint, ornamental, placid and easily managed, the Belgian bantam breeds are ideal for suburbia. They come in complex colour combinations and have an owl-like face, due to the profuse face feathering and mane-like neck hackles. Hens and roosters look quite similar.

The Belgian bantams have restricted vision because of the profusion of facial feathering and this makes them easy prey for predators. They are best kept on a neat lawn and need dry quarters when it' s wet.

The feather-legged d' Uccle doesn' t scratch much, is the most placid and least active of the three varieties of Belgian bantam, and is the best to let loose in the garden. Belgian bantams are only fair layers. **32**.

Brahma

This big placid Asian bird has full leg and foot feathering. It looks like a light Sussex wearing trousers! The breed has a fair laying ability, gives a cream-to-brown egg and is hardy in cold weather. It actually died out in Australia but is currently being redeveloped. **14**.

Campine

The Campine, pronounced ' campeen' , is another ornamental fowl of Belgian origin. The breed is very alert, active and hardy, but is also friendly enough to adapt to being confined. Gold and Silver varieties exhibit a green-black barring pattern that encircles their bodies, and both sexes present the same colour pattern. Campines are reasonable layers of relatively large white eggs. They are excellent foragers but are rather flighty and non-broody. Chickens feather up so quickly that feather picking and cannibalism can be a probem – in which case you should provide plenty of protein and distractions. A smallish breed that is now fairly rare, the Campine would be ideal in a ' tractoring' cage system. **8**.

Cochin

The Cochin is a heavy Asiatic breed that arrived in England in the 1840s and enjoyed great popularity there for a while. The Cochin looks a bit like an Orpington, but is taller and more profusely feathered. It comes in a variety of colours – Buff, Black, White and Blue – and lays a pinkish-tinted egg. The Cochin is a very sedate breed and is easily contained. It is a reasonable layer, with good broodiness and mothering abilities. It died out in Australia but is being redeveloped.

Croad Langshan

This massive, upright Asian bird is one of the tallest of the pure breeds and is rather expensive to feed. Black is the most common colour, although there are also White and Blue varieties. Croad Langshan eggs are plum-brown.

Dorking

This classic breed was introduced into England some 2000 years ago and has changed little since then. A heavy breed with five toes on each foot, it is quite stately, with a big rectangular body and short legs.

The Dorking is a medium layer, a slow grower, and is placid and gentle. It does not scratch excessively, but is still a good forager.

Chicks are shy and timid, and need plenty of space. They are not known for their hardiness and must have dry quarters. Hens are good broodies and mothers. Male chicks have lighter down colour than females. Both sexes are very slow to feather up. **34.**

Faverolles

The ' Fav' is an exotic French breed that exhibits early maturity and fast growth. It is a medium size, dual-purpose bird. Its body is chunky and rectangular, and its legs are short.

With its owl-like feathered face, feathered legs and five toes, the Faverolles is highly ornamental. Salmon is the most common colour pattern. Favs also come in White, Black, Buff, Ermine and Cuckoo colours, although these varieties are extremely rare. The sexes have contrasting plumage colours.

The Fav is very docile, quiet and non-aggressive. It is hardy, especially in cold weather, and adapts to various climates and also to confinement.

An average layer of cream-tinted eggs, hens can cover many eggs when sitting. They make persistent broodies and good mothers. Chicks are prone to being bullied by other breeds and should be kept separated. The chicks can be easily sexed from about 7 days of age as the female and male chicks have different coloured down. **17.**

Frizzle

This unique looking Asian bird has peculiar feathers that look as if they have been rubbed up the wrong way. This is because the feather shafts are curved, making the feathers face towards the head.

The Frizzle lays tinted or white eggs, but not in great abundance. This purely ornamental rare breed comes in many colours. **6.**

Hamburgh

A popular breed in the United Kingdom a century ago, the Hamburgh is a non-broody, medium layer of white eggs. This ornamental old breed is generally black/beetle green with white ear lobes and a rose comb, although there are four other colour varieties. The Spangled and Pencilled varieties are very beautiful. A smallish bird, the Hamburgh is hardy and vigorous, bold and alert. It matures early, and can be nervous and flighty. 21 and 35.

Houdan

A small but fast-growing French breed, the Houdan (pronounced ' oo-dan') is glossy black, with white mottling. A dual-purpose bird, it has a square body, five toes, a huge crest, beard and big muffs. The unusual butterfly comb looks like an open book. Related to the Polish, the Houdan is extremely docile and easily handled. 36.

Indian Game (Cornish Game)

Although somewhat aggressive, Indian Game are quiet and easily contained. Heavy birds, they have a very broad chest and thick legs, a bit like a bulldog. Only the Dark variety is common.

A poor layer of brown eggs, Indian Game make excellent broodies and mothers. They have been very popular in the past as table birds. 7.

Japanese Bantam

This tiny ornamental fowl is an ancient and unique Asian bird. A rare breed, it has the shortest legs of all fowl and a towering upright tail. It waddles around and is easy to handle -   great for kids.

Japanese Bantams are long-lived and their feathering improves with age. Laying only a dozen or so eggs before going broody, they make good mothers, although mating can be a problem unless you only keep a pair or have just one hen at a time with the rooster. Japanese Bantams need a clean, dry yard. 37.

Jersey Giants

Jersey Giants are massive birds –   cocks can grow to nearly 6kg –   that were developed in New Jersey, in the United States of America. There are Black, White and Blue varieties, although the latter is rare. Legs are ' willow' coloured (dark greeny yellow). Their hardiness, vigour and winter laying made them very popular as a dual-purpose breed in America in the 1930s.

Jungle Fowl

The small, rare Jungle Fowl *(Gallus gallus)* is the original South-East Asian bird from which domestic fowl are descended. Cocks are bold and aggressive with beautiful red, gold and black colouring. Hens are plain but daintily charming and often very friendly. They are poor layers of small, pink eggs. **9.**

Langshan

The Langshan is a big upright bird with feathering down the sides of its shanks. A dual-purpose breed, it is known for winter laying. Black Langshans are fairly common, while White and Blue varieties are now rare. **15.**

Leghorn

Leghorns and their crossbreds are the most populous fowl on Earth. A good to excellent layer of large white eggs, this classic Mediterranean breed with its big, erect comb has good fertility and matures rapidly. It is hardy, but noisy and excitable, and flightiness can be a problem. White is the most common colour; the beautiful coloured strains are becoming rare nowadays. **20.**

Minorca

Another Mediterranean breed, the Minorca is an excellent layer of large white eggs. It is non-broody. The Minorca is generally Black, although White is sometimes available. It has long legs and large white ear lobes hanging below the ear. **38.**

New Hampshire

A chestnut-coloured American breed that was developed for both meat and brown eggs, the New Hampshire is a medium-sized bird. Fast growing, vigorous and hardy, it makes a good broody and mother. **39**.

Old English Game

Bred from English fighting cocks not far removed from the primordial Jungle Fowl, these small birds are now kept mainly for exhibition. They are hardy and self-sufficient, make excellent broodies and mothers, but are only fair layers of rather small eggs. Cock birds, as you may have guessed from their ancestry, are very bold, being courageous to downright pugnacious. Feathering is tight, and they come in about 40 different colour combinations. Despite their small size they have quite good table qualities.

Orpington

A large, dual-purpose fowl from which the Australorp was bred, the Orpington is only a reasonable layer. With a heavy, fluffy body on short legs, it is easy to contain. Active, but gentle, the hens make fine broodies and mothers. Only the Buff Orpington is easy to come by. Blue and Black varieties are becoming rare. **44**.

Pekin

One of the most popular ornamental pet bantam breeds, the Pekin looks like a round ball of feathers, with fully feathered legs and toes. It is extremely placid, easily handled and contained. Often just kept for their broody qualities, Pekins make good mothers but are only average layers. The Black, Blue, Buff and White colour varieties are fairly common, while the Birchen, Cuckoo and Mottled colours are becoming rare.

With all that feathering, Pekins need a protected, clean and dry environment in order to thrive and look their best. **42**.

Plymouth Rock

A friendly dual-purpose breed, the placid Plymouth Rock was developed last century in America, where it is now rare.

The ' Rock' is hardy and very long-lived. It is a fair layer, an excellent broody and a good mother. Male chicks display slower feathering than females from about 10 days to 2 months of age. This makes them relatively easy to sex.

The Rock is easily contained but has a very hearty appetite so it isn' t the most economical breed to run.

The most well known variety is the Barred Rock, with its neat black-and-white barred feathers. The Dark Barred variety is the most common. The Light Barred variety is becoming rare and other varieties, such as the White, are extremely rare. 43.

Polish
This ornamental bird has a large crest, which obscures its vision. This makes it easy to contain. Coming in standard and bantam sizes, colours are White, White Crested Black, Chamois, Gold and Silver. A Frizzled form also exists.

The Polish needs a clean dry environment in which to really thrive. Not a utility bird, it nevertheless has tasty meat and lays a good-sized white egg. It is a ' non-sitter' , meaning it does not get broody. 4.

Rhode Island
Another classic barnyard fowl, this heavy breed is one of the best layers of all fowl and is a very popular dual-purpose bird. It is hardy, adaptable and active but is fairly docile and easily contained. Hens make good broodies and mothers; cock birds are unfortunately rather aggressive. The Rhode Island Red' s lustrous red feathers are most handsome. There is a White variety, but it is rare. 18.

Rosecomb
This tiny ornamental bantam breed is a jaunty, feisty bird. It is rather flighty and is non-broody. It is black, with a green sheen. There is also a White variety. The bird has large white ear lobes and a prominent rose comb. Eggs are few. Meat is scant but tasty. 40 and 41.

Sebright

Like Rosecombs, Seabrights are true bantams. They are also strictly ornamental. The Seabright sports a rose comb and hen feathering. Gold- and Silver-laced varieties have feathers edged with a narrow band of green-black. The Seabright is a poor layer of creamy white eggs. Excessive inbreeding has resulted in the eggs being of low fertility and hatchability. Hens make good broodies and mothers, however. 5.

Silkie

When it comes to feathered pets, the Silkie reigns supreme. With their striking good looks and gentle, quiet, placid natures, Silkies are real charmers.

Silkies are unique in having black skin and bones. They also have fluffy feathers, five toes and turquoise ear lobes. The White Silkie is most common, but Black is also popular. Colours such as Blue, Gold, Partridge and Buff are rare.

Silkies are in between standard and bantam in size, although rare bantam versions do exist. Their profuse feathering makes them look bigger than they actually are. Powder-puff crests obscure their vision and their short legs give them poor mobility. Predators can be a problem because of this. However, Silkies are easily contained and are happy to sleep on the ground, so only low fences, perches and nests are necessary.

A popular breed, Silkies have been around for quite a while. Marco Polo reported encountering them at the end of the 13th Century. 'Ukotsukei', as Silkies are known in their native China, are raised for the gourmet meat market and regarded as a delicacy.

Silkies are not known for their egg laying ability as they only produce about 12 eggs before going broody. They do this several times each year! The Silkies' tendency for broodiness is one of their best attributes, along with their outstanding mothering ability. They are often used to set eggs of flightier breeds and will impart their tameness to foster chicks.

In fact, it's a good idea to keep a couple of Silkie hens with your layers.

You will always be able to buy fertile eggs to raise more birds. One drawback, however, is that chicks sometimes get caught in the Silkie's feathers and can die this way.

Watch out for lice and scaly leg, to which Silkies are particularly prone. Their toenails will sometimes need to be clipped, as well. **23**.

Sussex

The Sussex is a very popular dual-purpose bird. It has good fertility, broodiness and mothering ability, and is very hardy, especially in cold climates. With so much feathering, hot climates don't suit the fluffy Sussex. It is gentle in nature and easy to contain.

Some Sussex strains have been selected for egg laying, others for meat. The chicks grow vigorously and they can be sexed at about 2 weeks – females having feathered up early, while males still have bare patches.

A traditional English breed, the Light Sussex is white with a black hackle, like a neck scarf, and is very popular in Australia. The Speckled, Red and Brown varieties are rare here. **10** and **13**.

Transylvanian Naked Neck

The bizarre looking Naked Neck has up to 40% less feathering than normal fowl. It frolics in the heat outdoors, when other breeds pant in the shade. Such fowl are still found wild in some Asian jungles and I've seen backyard birds scratching around in the rural villages of Malaysia.

Unfortunately, many people find the bare, red necks of this breed repulsive – a great pity, as Transylvanian Naked Necks are excellent layers, with a friendly temperament (although the bantam roosters can be very aggressive with other roosters). Standard fowl are active, but not too flighty, and also make good eating. The reduced plucking time from fewer feathers is a bonus! **16**.

Welsummer

A medium-sized fowl with colouring similar to that of the ancestral Jungle fowl, the Welsummer was developed in the Netherlands at the turn of the 20th century. **12**.

Welsummers produce as many as 160 large (up to 70g) brown eggs per year. They are docile, active and non-sitting, excellent foragers and economical layers. Although a light breed, they are not flighty.

Male chicks are distinguished by their lighter coloured down and not-so-distinct stripes.

Wyandotte

This cuddly looking bird is a great all-rounder. It is a reasonable layer and table bird, an excellent broody and mother, and a visual delight. The breed is docile and friendly, and requires only low fences.

Developed in North America, the Wyandotte is a large bird that enjoys great popularity. There are about 15 different colour varieties. The White, Gold Laced and Silver Laced are the most common in Australia. Partridge, Pencilled and Columbian varieties are becoming rare, while other colours are already rare. **1 and 20.**

Duck breeds

All of the domestic duck breeds, with the exception of the Muscovy, were initially bred from the wild Mallard. The Mallard is very colourful and is a strong flyer. Domestic breeds, apart from Muscovys, have had flying ability bred out of them.

Aylesbury

A pure white bird reaching massive proportions, the Aylesbury has a huge chest and deep keel that nearly touches the ground. It was one of the principal table ducks and often crossed with the Pekin for hybrid vigour. **25.**

Cayuga

This North American breed is black, with a stunning beetle-green sheen. The drake' s head is very green. Daffy Duck was probably modelled on this breed, which is heavy and ornamental, with good dual-purpose properties.

Fast growing, and laying a blue-green egg, the Cayuga is an excellent forager and very hardy. **11.**

Campbell

These ducks were the premier egg-laying birds in the 1930s, when they outclassed even laying fowl. In 1935, a top duck laid 327 eggs in 336 days!

Good in suburbia, this medium-sized duck starts to lay white eggs at 22– 24 weeks. Up to six or seven ducks are kept to one drake. Ducks may go broody, but are not trustworthy sitters. Fast growing, some strains may be flighty and nervous.

A dual-purpose breed of great popularity and a good forager, this duck was named after Mrs Campbell of Gloucestershire, England, who bred them for their utility properties. The popular Khaki Campbell is still common, although White Campbells are now rare and the Dark variety is critically rare in Australia. 27.

Elizabeth

An Australian breeder developed this duck recently, aiming for a small, fast-growing, ornamental bird. Derived from the Mallard, it looks similar to the Welsh Harlequin and Silver Appleyard. A good forager and economical to keep, the Elizabeth duck is a very good layer. It is also a good sitter and mother that likes to sit communally. 26.

Indian Runner

An excellent forager and egg layer, this medium-sized duck appears penguin-like because it stands so upright. It runs, rather than waddles and has a long neck that makes up about a third of its body length. There are several colour varieties. The White, and Fawn and White varieties are becoming rare, while Black, Chocolate, Fawn and Trout are extremely rare.

The Runner is an economical duck, a small and adept forager. It is one of the best breeds for garden pest control. It is hardy and adaptable to a range of climates and conditions. It is also active, nervous and non-broody and does not like being confined. .

Mallard
This colourful wild duck is the ancestor of all the duck breeds except the Muscovy. It is illegal to keep Mallards in some parts of Australia, so check with State departments of agriculture before obtaining birds. The Mallard is a strong flier.

Muscovy
The Muscovy *(Cairina moschata)* is the only domestic duck breed not derived from the Mallard. It is a South American bird and is classed as a perching duck, as opposed to the Mallard, which is a dabbling duck. Muscovys hiss instead of quack.

Muscovys are hardy economical birds. They are popular in Europe as table birds – their meat is tasty, low in fat and high in protein. Egg production is not high. The eggs take 35 days to hatch, a week longer than those of other ducks. The offspring of Muscovys crossed with other duck breeds are sterile.

The Muscovy' s featherless face has ugly bumps, called ' caruncles' , all over it. Drakes are huge, weighing up to 6kg and are very pugnacious. Females are only half the size of their male counterparts and are quite docile. They make great pets, broodies and mothers. Their quietness makes them good in urban areas but young birds are good fliers – you will need to clip their wings to keep them at home. Muscovies are good lawnmowers as they prefer to graze on grass. They will happily perch with fowl at night. Beware of their long, sharp claws when handling. 2.

Orpington
This medium-sized duck of an even buff colour is a dual-purpose bird that can lay 100– 150 eggs per year, although the best strains lay around 200. Developed in England at the turn of the century, the Orpington is hardy and fast growing. 24.

Pekin
This large white duck was primarily bred for meat, but it is also a good layer of pale blue eggs. Donald Duck was modelled after this cute, waddling Chinese duck. White, with bright orange legs and bill, it grows rapidly and breeds easily. A nervous bird, it is non-broody and

vulnerable to predators because of its slowness. Not a great forager, the Pekin needs a peaceful, safe environment and quiet handling. Because of its large awkward body, it' s best to give pond access to assist mating. **29**.

Rouen

A massive and majestic duck, the Rouen is the largest domestic breed and one of the most attractive. It is also the most placid. The Rouen drake is very colourful, looking like a Mallard, only brighter. The duck is mainly brown. The egg is tinted blue in colour.

Bred for meat and looks, the Rouen is slow to mature. It is also a poor layer and is non-broody. Because of its size and lack of agility, fertility can be low. This problem can be overcome by keeping a yearling drake with three or fewer ducks.

On the plus side, the Rouen will not stray far from home and is very easy to contain. **30**.

Silver Appleyard

This hardy duck, coloured like a pale Mallard, is a good layer of big eggs, and is easy to breed. A beautiful dual-purpose breed, it comes in standard and bantam varieties. **28**.

Welsh Harlequin

This breed was created from a ' sport' of the Khaki Campbell, probably a throwback to the original Mallard, which it resembles.

It is lighter than the Campbell, but its eggs are bigger. The female is creamy fawn in colour and is a sprightly forager. The big advantage of this breed is temperament. It is very placid and easily managed. Some of these ducks make wonderful sitters and mothers, but not all can be trusted to stay on the nest. **15**

Endnotes

[1] Miller, M. (comp.) 1996, *Rare and Minority Breeds of Poultry in Australia*, Australian Rare and Minority Breeds Association Inc., Elphinstone, Victoria.

1. Partridge Wyandotte hen

2. Blue Muscovy Ducks

4. White Crested Black Polish hen

3. Indian Runner drake

5. Silver Sebright Bantam rooster

6. Buff Frizzle bantam rooster

7. Jubilee Indian Game rooster

8. Gold Campine rooster

9. Jungle Fowl hen & rooster

10. Buff Sussex hen

11. Cayuga duck

12. Welsummer hen

13. Light Sussex rooster

14. Large Light Brahma hen

15. Willie the Welsh Harlequin drakeling

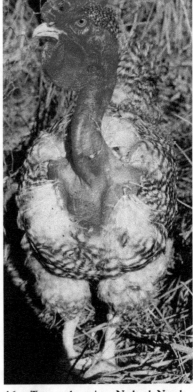

16. Transylvanian Naked Neck rooster

17. Salmon Faverolle hen

18. Rhode Island Red rooster

19. Black & Red Aracaunas

21. Gold Spangled Hamburgh rooster

20. Silver Laced Wyandotte bantam rooster

22. Lavender Aracauna hen & rooster

23. Silkie hen

24. Buff Orpington duck

26. Elizabeth duck

27. Khaki Campbell duck

25. Aylesbury drake

28. Silver Appleyard duck

29. Pekin duck

30. Rouen drake

31. Australorp bantam rooster

33. Barnevelder hen

32. Barbu d'Anvers

34. Silver Grey Dorking hen

35. Hamburgh hen

36. Houdan bantam hen

37. Japanese bantam hen

38. Minorca hen

39. New Hamshire pullet

45

40. Rosecomb rooster

41. Rosecomb hen

43. Dark Barred Plymouth Rock
bantam rooster

42. Blue Pekin hen

44. Orpington hen

Housing Backyard Poultry

Which system?

There are several management systems you can use for poultry. Select one that best suits both you and the site, and be well organised *before* poultry arrive.

Poultry are creatures of habit and, once settled into a system, they hate to be changed around or moved suddenly. If birds happen to be laying when moved, for instance, they'll do anything to get back to their old nest. So design well first.

The poultry system will need to take into account the following:
- How much area is available?
- How much access to your garden do you want the birds to have?
- What predators could you expect?
- What type of climate and seasons are experienced?
- What are the hottest/coldest temperatures?
- From which directions do the worst winds come from?
- Will you be breeding birds?

You will also need to consider some of the possible problems that can develop from the impact of poultry in the garden.

Which is best: a fixed or mobile home? There are advantages and disadvantages to both systems, and it depends on your situation. I think a combination is ideal, especially if you intend to breed birds.

Permanent houses and pens

Many people inherit an old backyard shed, which can be easily converted into a birds' night house with a few sheets of corrugated iron and some perches. Make sure you plug up all gaps and holes that predators might get in.

A permanent 'chook house'. The large tree provides shade in hot weather.

Perches should be at a convenient height in relation to the breed of bird. Silkies, for instance, cannot jump up too high to perch so their perches should be low.

Building with petrified hessian

A good old-fashioned method for wall making and hole plugging is to use ' petrified hessian' , which is more flexible and aesthetically pleasing than sheet iron.

To make a wall of petrified hessian, attach hessian or a similar material (potato bags are also good) to a solidly built frame and dampen it half an hour before beginning to coat it with cement. Do the job on a cool day or in the late afternoon when it is cool.

The formula calls for:
    5L water
    5.5kg cement
    900 g lime
    450g salt
    225g alum.

Sift the salt and lime through a fine sieve. Add the water and then the cement, stirring constantly, until the mixture is well blended. Then, stir in the alum.

Apply the concrete mix to the hessian immediately with a stiff brush, first on the outside, then on the inside. After the initial wetness disappears, but before the mix sets, apply a second coat to the outside. When this final coat sets, the material will be quite hard and strong. The mixture should cover 8m². Keep the surface damp for 3 days by spraying it with water.

Soil problems

Permanent housing/pen systems can result in soil problems. Land over-grazed by birds becomes unproductive. Fowl manure has a high fertiliser value, and too much fertiliser pollutes the soil. The manure is also very acidic, giving the soil a sour smell. Acidity frees-up toxic elements, such as aluminium, in the soil. (A sprinkle lime or dolomite on the soil will help to counteract acidity.) Few plants can survive over-manuring and most die.

Land over-grazed by birds also becomes eroded and compacted. Hard-packed soil has low fertility because it cannot absorb air. Healthy soil is dependent on being packed with aerobic microorganisms (4 billion in every teaspoonfull!), which need oxygen to breathe. A lively soil grows the best food and such organically grown produce has been proven to have the best food value, compared with chemically produced foods.

To avoid soil problems you might have to temporarily exclude birds from over-grazed areas by erecting fences; placing cages, wire or shadecloth over some spots; or by resting fowl yards entirely. Carefully monitor the birds' environmental impact. Remove droppings before they build up and, ideally, add them to compost to make an excellent plant food (instructions for making compost are provided in Chapter 10.).

Free-range poultry

Permanent night sheds can house birds that are allowed to free range through orchards or vegetable yards by day. This way you make positive use of their scratching and foraging to clear out spent vegetables, weeds and insect pests. But watch birds carefully, because after too much scratching, compaction will eventually occur. The heavier the breed, the worse it will be.

As long as you are not overstocking, a free-range poultry system with a permanent night house can work well. (A sustainable stocking rate on pasture is about 50 birds to the acre, but this number may not be intensive enough for vegetable bed tractoring.)

Areas immediately around the permanent shed will suffer the most wear and tear. A straw yard around the shed will greatly help, provided that the straw is regularly topped up.

With free-ranging fowl scratching around permanent plants, root zones can become exposed and young leaves pecked off. Ducks will dabble their beaks deep into compost and straw mulch. Design for prevention in this case.

Valuable plants may have to be caged or their mulch zones secured. A heavy mulch of sticks, branches, bark or rocks will provide useful protection around the root zone. A tyre or tree guard (such as a hessian bag) placed around plants will also help protect them. First work out just what you want to cage - the birds or the plants?

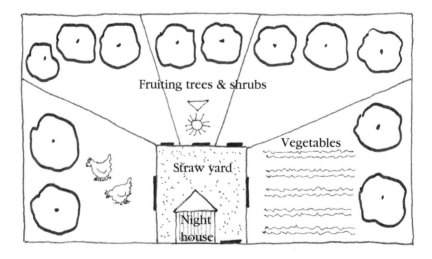

An ideal yard design: fowl can be given access to rotational yards to clean them up after vegetables are harvested.

'Tractoring' birds

If your garden is too precious for marauding poultry to free range in, ' tractoring' may be the answer.

Tractoring involves keeping birds in a moveable pen and moving the pen, and the birds, before manure reaches critical levels or compaction occurs. This way you also avoid a build-up of parasitic poultry worms (from the eggs in soil). A rest of 6 months should be enough to break the worm cycle.

Tractoring is a great system for a small area, or for protecting prized plants. You can also design vegetable garden beds to fit under mobile pens and allow birds to ' tractor' the bed after harvest. This system is also ideal for rearing little chickens or for keeping breeding families separated. Lawns benefit greatly from the light manuring as well.

Use an open bottomed pen that provides sun and rain protection, and caters for all the birds' needs. As long as it is moved around frequently the birds should be healthy and happy. You can always let them out for a few hours to allow them more exercise and foraging while you' re home.

A mobile pen made from steel and polypipe.

Mobile housing design

Mobile houses can be made from many easily found materials, in several styles, ranging from wooden boxes or crates, to polypipe tunnels and bamboo A-frames. They can be wire meshed all over, or covered with plastic, fishing net, or shadecloth. You can also buy mobile coops ready-made in steel.

In extremes of heat or cold, you may wish to provide a house with good insulation for greater comfort. A strawbale house as a semi-permanent fixture for a rotational yard may be the answer. It can be assembled quickly by stacking straw bales two high in a U shape. Place a few pieces of timber over the top, cover them with plastic or corrugated iron, then add a topping of straw ' biscuit' shingles for insulation.

Insert perches into the straw of this open-ended house, which ideally should have its open side facing north to catch the sun. Such a house should keep in good order for a long time, especially if rain is kept off the walls. If wind threatens to blow the structure apart, use ropes to tie it together or cover the top with a large tarpaulin, pegged well down at the corners.

Bamboo 'tractor' house. Together, the two halves provide a night house and outdoor run.

Home in a dome

A moveable pen system designed by permaculturist Linda Woodrow to integrate with her vegetable garden is based on the dome design.

Linda' s garden beds are circular and are intensively planted with rotating groups of companion plants of different ages. The aim is to have no gaps between plants and thus no bare, erodable soil. Weeds are pretty well suppressed in this way, and soil nutrients and moisture are conserved. Linda calls it a ' continuous polyculture' .

The domes work perfectly with the circular garden design. They are light in weight and are easily moved around. They function well even on sloping land.

The dome shape is easily created with PVC electrical pipe. A favourite design of Linda' s uses nine standard 6m lengths of 20mm pipe. This gives an area of 11.35m^2, with a height of 2m, into which a dozen or so fowl will fit happily. The circular shape gives the greatest internal area for the least circumference. In addition, bullies cannot harass and corner birds lower in the pecking order so easily, they just chase them in circles.

A dozen fowl can fit easily into this Linda Woodrow-designed dome.

The dome is totally covered in half-inch (13mm) bird wire to make it escape and predator proof. The small-gauge mesh is used to keep out snakes, the worst local predator. You can extend mesh out from the bottom rail across the ground, like a fringe, to stop burrowing predators. This ' fringe' can be weighted down with rocks or soil.

A door on the side is created from shadecloth sewn like a square tunnel tied in the centre. To throw in mulch or enter the dome Linda undoes the tie and pushes the tunnel inside the dome. To close up, she pulls the ' chute' out and ties it shut. This generally foils the carpet snakes.

Domes are moved fortnightly so that fowl can clean up spent garden beds and scratch loose the soil and mulch, readying them for the next crops. When scratching is complete, the pen is moved effortlessly. Linda just gets inside the dome, lifts it up and slowly walks it to the next site that needs ' chooking' , as she calls it. The fowl walk along with it. Each garden bed gets to be ' chooked' twice a year.

Linda' s moveable pen system allows for an ongoing supply of diverse vegetables and herbs, as well as delicious golden-yolked eggs.

Design for predators

Whether you decide on a fixed or mobile housing system, you must take into account the need to protect poultry from predators.

The style of housing employed depends a lot on what you are trying to keep in and out. It' s amazing what predators such as dogs, cats, foxes, snakes, big lizards and birds of prey are capable of! Find out what to expect by talking to local poultry keepers.

Foxes tend to strike in the early hours of morning or evening, and on moonlit or wet nights. If foxes are a problem, you may have to keep birds locked in until late morning and don' t leave them out too late in the evening.

Housing needs to be strongly made. Lightweight bird mesh may not be good enough. I have heard of foxes chewing through such mesh to get into an aviary. The house could be placed on stilts at about 1.5m, with

A predator-proof night house for a free-range flock is set up on 2.1m star pickets.

either a ramp or high landing perch for access. The ramp should be removed at night, of course. A good guard dog is a great asset, too.

Quolls are ferocious predators that suck the blood from their victims. These 'native cats' (marsupials) are pretty rare, although there is a colony in a patch of lantana in Vaucluse, Sydney. Birds need strong, roofed enclosures to be safe from them.

Most snakes are ground dwelling and rarely present a problem if perches are high enough, but pythons are something else! They are good climbers and can squeeze through small gaps or holes. They strangle their victims and swallow them whole. With their greatly increased girth the pythons then find themselves trapped inside the run until either the meal digests or you discover them.

When weighed down by their dinner, pythons are easy to catch and relocate. Just grab them behind the head and pop them into a bag. But keep those strangling coils away from you – they are incredibly strong.

You can't blame snakes for eating your birds if you haven't made them a safe house. Housing must be free of gaps and holes, with entrances high up, at about 1.5m. Smooth surfaces will deter snakes too, so vertical corrugated iron is a good material to build with. Never kill snakes, they are protected by law and are valuable for vermin control. Goannas are another difficult predator. They will bite and claw their way into poultry yards and clamber over most types of fence. They hunt out eggs and young birds to eat. One solution is to keep your poultry locked up in 'Fort Knox' until they have laid, then collect the eggs and release the birds. Another solution is to permanently keep your birds in a strong aviary or solid mobile pen.

Birds of prey to watch out for include not only all types of hawk and eagle, but also crows and kookaburras. Young poultry is never safe with them around, especially in spring, when predatory birds are also breeding. Fortunately other native birds, like magpies, don't like these predatory birds either and will bravely harass them.

Scarecrows and yapping guard dogs can help to keep birds of prey at bay. Plenty of shrub cover also helps, although birds like the brown goshawk can be swift forest hunters. The safest option is to roof poultry yards with wire mesh, anti-bird netting (designed for orchards) or shadecloth, etc.

Fencing tips
Housing may need to be solid, but fencing not necessarily so. A 1.8m (6ft) wire mesh fence with an electric wire on the outside will probably keep all land predators out. But maybe all you need is a 'floppy fence'.

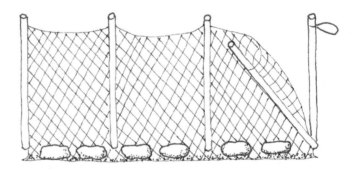

Floppy fences deter foxes from jumping into the fowl pen. A weighted fringe of wire mesh extending out from the bottom of the fence deters burrowing animals from entering. The floppy gate has a step-through position (illustrated) but also opens fully so that you can enter with the wheelbarrow.

Rock foundations prevent
burrowing predators from
getting into this poultry yard.

Willow cuttings planted closely
together form a living fence.

The bottom of a floppy fence must either be buried underground some
15cm (6in), or bent out across the ground and held down with rocks,
branches, logs or planks (which are best tied on). This is to deter
burrowing predators and bandicoots. Bandicoots are attracted by the
smell of food and attempt to burrow under the fence. If they succeed
and you don' t notice the burrow, a snake or goanna might find it first
and wreak havoc.

The other important component of a floppy fence is its floppy top. The
wire is left unstrained and loose. Foxes and birds are reluctant to jump
it. Floppy fences work well with floppy gates, which some people call
Queensland gates. Gates can be made with two opening positions, one
for stepping through and the other fully open for wheelbarrow access.

If you are considering electric fencing you must be prepared for the
constant upkeep. Electricity may short out if anything touches the fence
so it must be kept clear underneath. As weeds tend to thrive along
fence lines, this could be problematic.

You might decide to go the other way and have a ' living fence' . Plant a
lattice of willow or mulberry cuttings to keep birds in. A hedgerow of
thorny or unpalatable plants will also be fairly impenetrable. Rows of
smaller plants such as lemongrass (a clumping herb) or native
raspberries also make a good living fence, but they are not guaranteed
to be predator proof.

Living fences are much more aesthetic than post and wire fences, but wire fences can be made more aesthetic and are multi-purpose when used as trellises for vines, berries, peas and beans.

Water features can repel many predators. Ponds, creeks and ditches can be used as invisible fences for fowl, as well as creating scenic views.

Wherever possible situate fences along contour lines, rather than across them, to minimise the potential for erosion

Getting set up for ducks

Ducks can be kept in much the same set-up as fowl. The good news is that, because they are less destructive than fowl in the garden, they are better to have free ranging around it, using a permanent shed for a night house.

Ducks don' t perch and just need some straw or sawdust spread over the shed floor. You could keep them out in the open as they have waterproof feathers. However, ducks are nervous creatures and light disturbs them at night, so unless they sleep under some shady trees you can expect them to start quacking when a full moon appears, or when

Provide a full bucket of fresh water for ducks,
deep enough to duck their heads into for a wash.

car headlights disturb them. Herding them into a dark night house will give you a better night's sleep. When they become accustomed to the routine they'll herd themselves in each evening, but remember to shut the door for them.

Fencing ducks in is easy, as they only require a 1m high fence. Portable fencing systems can work well if ducks are needed to intensively garden in one section. This way many snails and slugs, for example, can be eliminated and turned into a food source for your ever-hungry ducks.

Ponds for ducks

Many people think that you need a pond to keep ducks. While it is not essential, it can assist breeding, as ducks are designed to mate afloat.

As long as you provide a full bucket of fresh water for them, deep enough to dunk their heads in for a wash, as well as somewhere to swim in the breeding season, they'll be fine.

Of course a duck would argue the point. A pond or bath is certainly great for keeping clean, and having lots of fun. It can provide the ducks' owners with hours of entertainment, too.

Some people build their ducks small permanent ponds by digging a hole in the ground (or burying a tyre) and lining it with plastic or concrete. I think this is a mistake, because the need for constant cleaning creates so much work. If water is allowed to go putrid, ducks will become sick from drinking it and die. Better to use a lightweight water container from which you can easily pour the murky contents over thirsty plants.

An old plastic baby's bath, or a cut down 200L drum, makes a good portable bath for up to half a dozen ducks. Plastic water containers break down in sunlight, so keep them in a shady spot for extended life.

If the bath is placed on bare earth, ducks will bore holes in the ground and dabble muddy beaks in the bath. You will have to wash it out constantly. Placing the bath on a concreted or gravelled area is one solution to the problem. Better still, put it in a different place – under a different fruit tree, perhaps – each day. Ducks will relax there in the heat of the day and deposit valuable manure directly onto the plants.

Water plants and ducks can co-exist.

There is a way to have a permanent pond system that is self-cleaning, while it automatically irrigates the garden. This system works best on a sloping site. Bury an old bathtub or shower basin uphill, with a pipe coming from the water outlet to the surface downhill. This pipe can then be connected to leach beds, distributed by agricultural pipe (slotted all over), or else have a hose connection for hand watering. All you have to do is pull out the plug. If ducks dabble at the plug they may be able to pull it out, too, and you may have to place a rock over it.

A word of warning... when ducks splash around in their bath they often displace the water level. Water containers generally have vertical sides and if an exit ramp or rocks are not provided ducklings may drown, especially if they are not fully feathered. Water bowls and buckets will do the same for any tiny young poultry and drowning is a common occurence if one isn' t careful.

To prevent drowning, place a rock or stick (but never a brick as it will leach toxic chemicals) in water containers when birds are young. Alternatively, put out very shallow water bowls as well as the usual containers. In larger or more permanent ponds you could use a float valve to keep water at the same height as the access level.

If you have an existing pond surrounded with beautiful water plants, you may consider ducks too destructive and totally inappropriate there. However, this may not necessarily be the case. Perhaps you can fence off most of the pond, leaving a small area of water accessible to the ducks. Ducks will get to swim and frolic, while water plants on the other side of the fence will benefit from the liquid manure.

Underwater pond fencing can be made with mesh (as seen overleaf) or shadecloth. Pin it down with rocks at the bottom of the pond.

One problem that can arise in a natural pond is that ducks will constantly dabble at the banks, eroding them away and enlarging the pond, which will grow progressively shallower. If vegetation cannot survive dabbling you may have to line the banks with rocks, or with shadecloth or hessian cloth pegged down.

To keep the setting natural you might first establish suitable waterside plants which can grow through holes in the cloth or between rocks and help to stabilise the bank. It's best to wait until vegetation has established before you introduce the waterfowl. Otherwise, if you can't wait, you might cage off individual plants until they are firmly rooted.

Feeding Backyard Poultry

Don't make the mistake in thinking that kitchen scraps and garden forage will be enough to sustain your poultry. No matter how natural and well established your backyard poultry system is, foraging for a full range of nutrients necessary for optimum health won't usually be possible for your birds. Green feed alone can only substitute for up to 10% of commercial feed, so birds need supplementary feeding. Underfeeding leads to lower egg output, sickness and/or death.

Nutritional requirements

Birds require energy that's derived from carbohydrates and fats. In general, grains supply this requirement for carbohydrates and fats. Whole wheat, given from the age of 3 weeks, is excellent.

Birds also need protein to develop. Proteins are based on 11 essential amino acids and other non-essential amino acids. Growing birds and layers require a diet composed of 15 - 16% protein, increasing to 18% in hot weather when they eat less. Chicks need a diet with 20% protein.

Pellets and crumbles are the most convenient way of supplying protein. Meat, at about 50% protein, is also a good source of protein and has the added advantage of containing phosphorus. As ducks and fowl are mostly omnivorous, they relish meat meal. Skim milk powder is another suitable source of animal protein.

Meat and bone meal may contain antioxidants and various other contaminants. Fish meal, another good source of protein, may contain heavy metals. If you are concerned about these contaminants, or prefer not to feed meat to your poultry, you can substitute these protein sources with vegetable seeds that are high in protein.

Vitamins, minerals and trace elements are also essential for health, but only small amounts are required. In a diverse free-range system many will be self-foraged. Commercial feeds often contain artificial vitamins and minerals. These come with preservatives, which tend to oxidise with age. So if the commercial mixes aren' t fresh, birds not on the free range may become vitamin and mineral deficient.

A natural alternative in a home-mixed diet is to add dried, powdered seaweed, comfrey and/or nettle powder. Brewer' s yeast can be added for protein and B vitamins. Wheat bran is another good ingredient, providing protein, zinc, manganese and phosphorus. Cod liver oil, a good tonic and source of vitamin A, can be added at weekly intervals. Mix it in with the feed at the last minute to avoid oxidisation.

The addition of other tonic herbs in the diet will also provide vitamins, minerals and trace elements.

Types of feeds
Poultry feeds can generally be classified into the following types:
* coarse grains
* pellets and crumbles
* wet or dry mash
* scraps
* insects
* green forage.

Poultry also need fresh water, plus grit to help digest foods.

Grains
While wheat can be served whole, most common grains must first be broken up to be digestible. Maize must always be fed at least cracked, oats should be clipped (or sprouted) and the awns of barley should be removed. Mixed, coarse grain is the easiest form to buy. It makes a good scatter feed – throw it around where you want birds to scratch the ground.

If you make your own mix it will have to be seasonally adjusted. In summertime barley and corn are too heating, so less should be fed. In wintertime feeding increases as the temperature drops below 21°C. A drop of 10°C will increase feeding by 15%, so give birds more grain when it' s cold. Wheat, which is low in protein, is best.

Grain substitutes

Grain growing in massive monocultures is not sustainable, with tonnes of topsoil regularly lost or polluted. Organic grains are available, but are costly to buy. Any reduction in commercial grain use does the environment a favour.

Grain substitutes include cooked root vegetables such as carrots, potatoes, Jerusalem artichokes, parsnips, cassava root*, turnips and sweet potato. Some root vegetables, such as sweet potato and carrot, are fine to eat raw, but they will need to be nailed or tied up on a wall for easier pecking. A traditional fattening food is one part bran to four parts cooked potato. The grated roots of mullein, a common garden weed in Australia, also make a fattening energy food.

Pellets

Pellets and chick crumbles may be the most artificial type of feeds, but they are also the most convenient, providing the necessary protein levels for growing and laying. Pellets tend to be the least popular of all feedstuffs. To counteract this, feed pellets before grain, or they may not be eaten. Alternatively, soak the pellets for about 5 minutes in water or milk to create a mash suitable for birds of all sizes. Make sure you use the mash as quickly as possible, before the wet meat meal sours.

If birds are given free choice of grain and pellets, kept in separate containers, they will be able to self-select a balanced diet according to their individual needs. Hang feed containers from above so that rats can' t access them. In this way you can go away and leave birds for a weekend.

Mash

Wet mash is a traditional feed. It is a mixture of powdered grains and meals, served with an equal quantity of liquid, such as water, milk, buttermilk or meat soup, enough to give it a crumbly consistency. In wintertime mash can be warmed by adding hot liquid. It needs to put in a high-sided trough to stop spillage.

---

* Bitter cassava varieties are toxic and must be washed and cooked. Boiling or roasting the peeled roots renders them edible. Sweet cassava roots can be eaten raw after peeling.

Three mash recipes are outlined below.

Recipe 1.
  60 % ground wheat
  20% bran and wheat pollard
  20% meat meal

Recipe 2.
  65% mixed grain
  7% alfalfa meal
  8% meat or soya meal
  6 % ground oyster shell (shell grit) or limestone
  3% bone meal
  1% trace mineral
(For young birds, increase alfalfa meal and reduce oyster shell.)

Recipe 3.
  2 parts pollard
  1 part bran
  half part oaten pollard
  quarter part maize meal
  1.5 parts chaffed greenstuff (lucerne or comfrey)

Mash is relished and is usually quickly scoffed down by birds. The disadvantage of mash is that it is messy and, if not eaten quickly, it goes off and is wasted.

Scraps
Household food scraps should be kept in small covered containers in the kitchen and given regularly to birds. Don' t let scraps go rotten first or birds could get botulism, which may be fatal. Don' t feed tea leaves, coffee grounds, rhubarb leaves, soap, salt or salted products to poultry.

Greens
Green feed is an important part of a natural diet. It makes yolks yellower, as well as providing extra protein, vitamin A, calcium, phosphorus, manganese and riboflavin. It provides exercise and interest to foraging birds, preventing them from developing destructive ' vices'
– habitual neurotic behaviour.

If birds don't have access to free range, then give greens daily, about 50g per bird. To prevent the greens from being trampled, hang them up in a bunch, or put them in a hanging basket made of wire netting fixed at bird head height. Greens are most palatable when young and succulent, and must be fed fresh.

Lawns are a good source of greens, if mown at regular intervals and if chemicals have not been used on them. Ideally, cut grass with a hand mower – the scissor action doesn't mush the grass up, as does the motor mower. When putting birds out onto lawn, remember that they can only eat short, young grass. Tough, long grass is not very nutritious and may get caught in their crop.

Many greens are worth growing specially for birds. Lucerne can be grown in the summer, oats and barley in the winter. Canola, millet (use packets of bird seed), chou moellier, silverbeet, cabbage and a mixture of grasses and clovers can also be grown. To make them palatable, chaff or chop them up first. Don't just throw a large heap down, because it may go mouldy very quickly. Dispose of any uneaten remains after 12 hours.

Greens must be fed fresh. To prevent them getting trampled, hang them up in a bunch.

Sunflower heads can be hung up to be pecked at. The young green leaves also make succulent feed that can be finely minced and added raw to mash. Or dried leaves can be rubbed into powder and added to mash.

Comfrey

Protein-rich comfrey, a nutritious tonic food, is a good source of the amino acids tryptophan, lysine and methionine. It also has high levels of potassium and calcium (more calcium than alfalfa). Comfrey has long been used as food for humans, pigs and poultry.

Fowl fed a daily ration of comfrey before their grain enjoy good health and yield yellower yolked eggs. Pullets mature more quickly on comfrey and meat birds have yellower flesh (from the vitamin A in comfrey). Birds can self-forage this herb, or have bunches hung up for them to peck at. You can also slice up a bunch finely, like coleslaw.

Comfrey is unique among plants in that it contains vitamin B_{12}, an important vitamin for vegetarians. There is about half a microgram of B_{12} in every 100g of comfrey.

Comfrey also contains very low levels of poisonous alkaloids, with the roots having the greatest concentration. Such alkaloids are also found in other common foods, such as green potatoes, and are quite unstable. Wilting the leaves before use reduces the alkaloid levels and cooking destroys them. Despite this, animals have safely eaten the fresh herb for millenia. Elephants, for example, are fed more than 45kg of comfrey daily at Whipsnade Zoo, London, without any ill effects. (Unfortunately, the Australian government has scheduled comfrey as a mild poison.)

Insects

A good backyard food forest will harbour plenty of insects and these make good free tucker, high in protein. You can also trap bugs to feed poultry. Lay boards on the ground for a few days and turn them over to reveal a feast. Termites are a welcome treat. Birds can be used to patrol under the house and eradicate these pests.

Worms, too, make a good high-protein meal and will be much appreciated. You can breed them up yourself, see Chapter 10.

Water

Poultry need to drink a cup or two (half a litre) of fresh water daily. Hens deprived of water will stop laying. In summer, keep water containers in the shade, especially plastic ones. In places where cane toads are prevalent, place water high up so they cannot bathe in it.

Ducklings need a continuous supply of fresh, clean, cool water. If deprived of water for a few hours they are likely to gorge themselves on their next bowlful, which can cause cramps, collapse and even death. The excessive drinking distends the small intestine, causing intense pain and eventual heart failure from reflex nerve effects.[1]

If you find ducklings desperately thirsty, just give small amounts of water and a little food.

Grit

Insoluble grit, such as sand or small stones, provides a means to grind up food in a bird's gizzard. A good type to buy is flint grit, or basalt crushings. Less grit is needed by birds kept in regions of sandy soil.

Grit and calcium for egg production can be supplied in the form of limestone grit, finely ground oyster shell (shell grit) or roasted, crushed eggshells. If feeding eggshells, you must remember to crush them so that the hens don't learn to recognise eggs as food and become egg eaters themselves!

How much to feed fowl

It is good to feed your birds on an 'ad lib', or 'as needed' basis. In order to work out how much feed is actually required, observe the birds feeding and see how much feed is left uneaten. If a great deal of feed is left over, you obviously need to reduce the amount of feed given. If all the feed disappears very quickly, you need to increase the amount given.

Of course, you will have to make sure all have access to a feed bowl without crowding or bullying, and keep an eye on the timid ones who may miss out. The larger the flock, the more problems like this will arise, and more feed bowls will be required.

As grains take longer to digest, a common feeding regime is to give a handful of wet mash per bird in the morning and a handful of mixed grains per bird in the evening. A small handful will do for a bantam, a large one for a standard sized bird.

Buying feed in 40kg bags will reduce costs, but you must keep it well stored; dry, cool and vermin free. Dried leaves of plants with insecticidal properties can be scattered amongst feed as a pest repellant. Use white cedar, neem, rosemary and the like. Experiment with other aromatic leaves, such as strongly scented melaleuca / tea tree or eucalyptus.

Feeding young chickens

Proprietary crumble provides a convenient balanced diet for little chickens, having the necessary 20% protein, although it also contains a coccidiostat medication. Chicks like to eat about five meals daily at least, making it much easier to simply provide proprietary crumble ad lib.

In the first days a more natural feed is rolled oats, but don' t overdo it or the oats may paste up their vents. Soft fruits and kitchen scraps (plain food) will also be appreciated. Chickweed is a dainty wild salad green, just perfect for their tastes. Another traditional first food is boiled egg, plus breadcrumbs and milk. For the first week enough of this is put in shallow dishes as will be finished in 5 or 10 minutes.

' Kibbled' or ground hard wheat is good for chickens of up to 9 weeks of age. Chopped chives, boiled rice and small seeds are an excellent supplement to kibbled grain. You can also add raw milk and eggs to chick food, or make egg custard with onions, chopped dandelion, parsley and a little honey.

At 1 week some whole grain should be added to the chicks' ration. The amount of grain should be gradually increased until it comprises up to 40% of the diet by the time the chicks are 3 weeks of age.[2] When the chicks are 4- 8 weeks of age you can add some whey powder to the food to help prevent coccidiosis. At 2 months birds can go out on the free range and at 3.5 months they need an adult ration, which can be provided in the form of equal parts pellets or high-protein mash and grain.

Feeding ducks and ducklings

Feed requirements of ducks are basically the same as those of fowl.

Flaked oats plus a little bran, moistened, is a traditional first food for ducklings. After 2 days add pollard to the mix and moisten it with milk.

The coccidiostat drugs added to chicken crumble do not agree with ducklings, nor are they necessary. Try to get unmedicated crumble, such as a grower ration for older birds.

Vegetarian diet

Long ago people did not feed meat meal to poultry. William Cobbit wrote in his 1822 book *Cottage Economy* of the traditional foods given. These included warm boiled barley, curds, buckwheat, parsley and other herbs chopped fine, as well as chopped leeks, apples, pears, hemp and nettle seed, dried nettle in summer, boiled nettle in winter, and barley meal soaked in milk for fattening.[3]

It is possible to replace meat products in a commercial diet with soya, safflower or sunflower meal. Up to 10% of the diet can be made up with sweet lupins, or mung, adzuki or black gram beans – all are excellent protein complements to a cereal-based diet.

Acacia (wattle) seeds are about 23% protein and can also be good to supplement a vegetarian diet, although not all species may be suitable. [4]

In tropical climates, pigeon peas can be used for up to around 25% of the diet, and alfalfa and comfrey meal are also good. Sweet cassava leaves are high in protein, plus vitamin A.

Plant protein sources tend to have less lysine and vitamin B_{12} than meat sources, but fortunately comfrey is the exception. Phosphorus is also low in plant materials, but can be supplied in the form of low-fluoride rock phosphates. Do not give birds raw phosphate.

Tonics
Tonic herbs
There are many vitamin- and mineral-rich herbs with tonic properties that can be fed to poultry. Often the same herbs are used for similar purposes in humans and animals alike. They can be given at regular intervals and more often during periods of stress (when birds are moulting or laying, in cold or wet weather, etc). Fresh herbs can be grown in yards and, when needed, can be finely chopped and added to mash, or tied in bunches to be pecked at.

General tonic and laying stimulant herbs include garlic, onion, nettles, chickweed, raspberry leaf tea, aloe vera, dandelion, vetch, fennel, mint, wormwood, rue (good in a bran mash), cleavers, cress, marigold, sage, vervain, comfrey, sheperd's purse, mullein roots, thyme, marjoram, oregano, nasturtium, mugwort, goat's rue, seaweed, pigweed, gotu kola, yarrow and parsley. (Herb teas can be made for birds to drink also.)

To stimulate birds in cold weather, give them a mixture of one part black pepper in forty parts cornmeal. Alternatively, try adding chopped onions to their mash once or twice a week.

Tonics for chicks
For disease and parasite prevention, chicks will benefit from being offered a bowl of milk each morning. And a mix of some of the following tonics can be added to feed every few days to boost health and vitality:
- raw egg
- finely chopped garlic, rue and/or onions
- chopped herbs, such as fennel, chickweed, dill, mint, anise or rue
- seeds of grass, celery, millet, mustard, anise, shepherd's purse, sunflower, fenugreek, fennel, pigweed, canola and thistle
- raisins, powdered seaweed, flaked nuts or plantain
- pepper, chilli ginger, cayenne or paprika (in cold weather)
- apple cider vinegar (ideally organic and unpasteurised, add to water)
- aloe vera (crush it and add pulp to water)
- manuka honey (a teaspoon in water)
- raspberry cordial or juice (dilute to 1 in 10 parts water)
- cod liver oil
- mashed, cooked carrot, or raw carrot finely grated.

Tonics for moulting

Feathers are replaced annually, with moulting usually taking place in autumn. Birds may also go into moult in response to shock, heat, excessive stress or lack of water. They lose 60 - 100g of feathers, which are comprised of 85% protein. So feed to support the demands of the body for feather growth. All feathers should have regrown within about two months. When large areas of skin are exposed for long periods, moulting has been excessive.

Feed tonic herbs generously to encourage the growth of new feathers. The best herbs to choose from include seaweed, nettle, onion, garlic, dill, anise, cleavers, maidenhair fern and fennel. Sunflower seeds are good and they can be mashed and mixed with milk. Cabbages and turnips are also helpful. Avoid excessive corn, which can lead to cystine deficiency (cystine is abundant in meat, soya and fish meal).

A cup of brewed rosemary or southernwood with a little apple cider vinegar added to water on a weekly basis is an excellent plumage tonic.

Linseed is a good traditional moulting tonic. After initial soaking for 4 hours, cook a cupful of linseed gently in 1 litre (2 pints) of simmering water for 20 minutes, until it becomes a jelly. Add it to a wet mash to encourage the growth of new feathers – about a dessertspoonful per bird will suffice. Linseed should not make up more than 5% of the diet or it will have a laxative effect. It has to be cooked to destroy the pyridoxine inhibitor in it.

Bare skin areas can be rubbed with a lotion of 2 parts burdock brew mixed with 1 part castor oil. [5]

Endnotes

[1] Burton, H.W. 1992, ' Ducklings Can Drink Themselves to Death' , *Australasian Poultry*, June– July, vol 3, no. 2, p. 28.

[2] Cumming, Prof. R. 1991, ' Can Coccidiosis be Controlled by Nutrition?' , *Australasian Poultry*, Dec., vol 2, no. 5, p. 8.

[3] Cobbit, W. 1822, *Cottage Economy,* Oxford University Press, New York.

[4] Maslin, Thomson, McDonald and Hamilton-Brown, *Edible Wattle Seeds of Southern Australia*, CSIRO 1998, p. 12.

[5] Glos, K E., *Remedies for Health Problems of the Organic Laying Flock*, USA (online)

Breeding Backyard Poultry

Why take up poultry breeding? It may be just for the sheer pleasure of observing those tiny balls of fluff scampering about, shepherded by their adoring, watchful parents. Or you might find that there is a buoyant market for selling purebred chicks or ducklings.

You may also find that you want to replace your good but old layers with their younger progeny. If so, don' t expect to breed true to type from crossbred birds because, like hybrid plants, their characteristics have not been fixed. You' ll have more luck with purebred birds.

You may not ' decide' to breed at all and leave it all up to nature. Then you may get a nice surprise one evening when a missing hen returns from wild parts with a new brood and begging you for dinner.

Breeding fowl

Hens begin to lay eggs at about 6 months of age, at which stage they are known as ' point-of-lay' birds. The first year' s eggs are usually rather small. The hens will continue to lay eggs for several years, but after the second year productivity drops off. If you want to maintain levels of egg production you' ll need to breed replacement birds regularly. Every second year is a good idea.

Always provide nests that are cosy and attractive, or eggs will be laid elsewhere. The nest materials should be soft, as hens actually ' lay' when standing up so eggs can break if laid onto a hard surface. Why not line the nest with dried aromatic and insecticidal herbs?

As you gather eggs, never totally empty the nest or the hen will seek another more private location. Always leave a ' dummy' egg in the nest (don' t worry – she won' t miss the others). You can buy plastic or concrete eggs for this purpose, or you could save money and simply use boiled eggs or avocado seeds.

The breeding season usually begins in late winter or spring (depending on when the hen was hatched) and continues through into summer.

When breeding heavy breeds of fowl you will need a small rooster-to-hen ratio, about 12 hens maximum for each rooster. A lighter breed of rooster can maintain fertility with as many as 15 hens. After the second year, rooster fertility is much reduced and they are best replaced after 3 years. Alternatively, as roosters age, keep them with fewer hens to ensure fertile eggs.

One mating with a healthy young rooster is often enough to fertilise all the eggs laid for the following week. However, not all hens will lay fertile eggs. Some roosters have an aversion to certain hens; likewise some hens can't abide certain roosters.

The mating game
The mating game is a colourful spectacle. A vigorous cock dances, struts and circles around hens in his flock, chortling and displaying his feathering. A young cockerel will mate 30 to 40 times a day on the range and in good weather.

The hen will also become amorous when she starts to lay, crouching down to invite the cock to mount her, her wings and tail fluttering seductively.

Some roosters cause damage to the hen when mating, as their toes and spurs gouge into her back. After this, hens may end up bare-backed and much less keen, avoiding the rooster like the plague. In this situation it's kinder to separate the rooster and the hen to give the hen some rest and recuperation.

You can also reduce the problem by snipping, filing or grinding off the ends of sharp spurs and trimming the rooster's toenails occassionally.

The broody
When her hormones dictate it and conditions are right, a hen will go broody, sitting tight on the nest to incubate her eggs. This is usually

after she has laid a good clutch of eggs, whether they are fertile or not. If you have already eaten the eggs, leaving her with just a dummy egg, she' ll sit anyway. If it happens in springtime all the better – the new generation hens should become winter layers.

You can leave nature to do its work with a hen' s own eggs, or you can switch her eggs for others. If you decide to switch the eggs, check the hen' s seriousness before placing a good egg setting under her. If she stays tight on the nest and makes angry protests when approached, and if her breast is bare (because she has been plucking out her down to line the nest), she is probably well and truly clucky.

If the hen is clucky, make sure she is free of lice, which will become intolerable for her over time as she won' t have a chance to dustbathe. You could also line nest boxes with some aromatic herbs such as pine needles, dried tansy, lavender, pennyroyal and the like. These herbs deter pest insects.

If necessary, take the hen to a better nest site, but only ever move her at night. If possible, keep other hens from laying in the nest by isolating her. Putting a cage over the nest may be the answer. This is also a good idea if her nest is in a wild spot and vulnerable to predators.

The unwanted broody
The natural tendency to broodiness ensures a rest from egg laying and thus makes a healthier hen. Uninterrupted laying, as is bred for in modern laying hybrids, can lead to laying fatigue, cancer, leucosis, and increased mortality.

However, a hen sitting for long spells trying to hatch a concrete egg can also get out of condition. If you don' t want her to hatch eggs you will have to convince the hen to forget her broodiness. Put her in a bare wire cage in a bright spot and she will not feel like nesting for long.

But it may take as many days as she was broody before she gives up, so try and discover unwanted broodiness as early as possible and do something about it quickly. Feed and water as usual.

Breeding without a rooster

It is not always possible to keep a rooster, but it is still possible to have chicks. There are several options. You can:

- borrow a rooster for a week or two
- buy fertilised egg settings and put them under clucky hens
- let a hen sit for a couple of weeks on ' dummy eggs' , then slip some day old hatchery chicks under her in the night. She' ll get a lovely surprise the next morning!

Breeding ducks

Ducks generally start laying at about 8 months of age. A ratio of one drake to four ducks is a suitable ratio for heavy breeds; while up to eight ducks per drake is suitable for the lighter, egg-laying breeds.

A dual-purpose or ' table breed' of duck usually retains its instinct to go broody and can be generally relied upon to hatch a brood. The ducks of egg-laying breeds seldom go broody, however you can hatch their eggs under a broody hen. In this case, make sure there is high humidity in the nest by spraying warm water over the eggs when the broody goes off to feed, especially in hot dry weather and before hatching.

Two broody ducks share the same nest box.

Most advice on breeding fowls can be applied to ducks.

I once had an endearing Cayuga duck called Hopi. When sitting on eggs she would always tell me that she was hungry, with her loud bleeting quacks. She would then come charging towards me all fluffed up and tail fanning out so that she would appear more ferocious, swiping at any bird that dared block her path. I would try to have the feed bucket ready by then and she'd honk madly until she got to it.

One day something went badly wrong. I watched Hopi as she waddled back to the nest after dinner, as usual, and flopped down onto the eggs. As she sat a couple of rotten eggs exploded, spreading stinking slime around the nest. Hopi honked loudly in dismay and grabbed the offending shells in her beak. Then she shot off the nest to dump them somewhere.

There was a real danger that Hopi would abandon the nest if the mess wasn't cleaned up, and that the other eggs could become infected with the bacteria and also rot. So I raced down to the nest with a damp, warm, rag and cleaned every egg as fast as I could before Hopi returned from rinsing her smelly beak. After a bit of sulking she did eventually return, to settle back on the eggs and hatch the rest of them successfully.

The egg setting

The best eggs to use for breeding (called an ' egg setting') come from the first 20 or 30 that are laid after the first moult. These will be of the optimum size, producing bigger, more robust hatchlings.

Only select eggs to set that are of normal size and free of any defects. These are best to set at between 2 and 7 days old, or at a maximum age of 2 weeks. The longer you keep them, the slower they are to hatch. When collecting setting eggs, avoid washing them as the pores will open and allow some of the dirt to soak in. Instead, clean dirty eggs with a dry abrasive cloth or wire wool. A rag dipped in warm water can be used briefly if other attempts fail. Ideally, don't set very dirty eggs.

Store the setting eggs in a cool, dry place, with the pointy end facing down. Never refrigerate them. It is best to store them on their sides at between 10° and 15°C, and turn them twice daily. Turning helps prevent the embryo from attaching to the membrane and sticking. It also assists with gas exchange.

An easy method for turning the eggs is to place the egg setting in an egg carton and prop up one end of the carton on something, like a brick. Turning, then, simply means alternating the raised ends of the carton.

Setting the eggs

When the hen is definitely broody you can slip an egg setting under her after dark. If the setting is too large, eggs will roll out and chill. A dozen is a good number. It will take about 2 days of constant warmth before the embryo begins to develop in the egg. The eggs will keep during this period, as long as they are turned regularly.

Incubating the eggs

The hen should get off the eggs occasionally to feed and perhaps take a quick dustbath. She can leave the eggs for up to 20 minutes without the eggs coming to any harm. Eggs are most vulnerable to stresses, including chilling, in the first week. An incubator may be more reliable at this time, as the hen may not be totally clucky and may wander off for extended periods.

A dozen or so eggs is a good number for an egg setting.

Conversely, some hens sit so tight on the nest that they starve to death. If your hen is not getting off the nest at all, you will have to lift her off the nest regularly. Silkies tend to sit very tightly and often foul the nest with droppings, but this can be avoided if you assist her.

When a hen does hop off her nest you can discretely check the eggs. Make sure the nest is well shaped so that the eggs cannot roll out. Check the eggs to see if dot-like lice are crawling over them. Apply an insect repellent to your hands and arms if you don' t want lice crawling on you. Even if the hen appears to be free of lice, give her a couple of good lice treatments just to be sure.

Any mess found in the nest should be cleaned up and dirty eggs wiped with a warm, moist rag. Try not to totally remove the egg' s protective membrane when doing this. If you only feed the broody hen wheat or mixed grain, her droppings will be less offensive.

During incubation the hen turns the eggs up to 100 times a day. Oil from her bare breast will coat them, helping to prevent moisture loss. The eggs soon become quite shiny. A few days before the chicks start to pip their way out of the shell, they don' t need to be turned anymore and temperature fluctuations won' t affect them so much.

Hatching the chickens

If all goes well, after about 21 days (28 for ducks) of incubation your eggs should have hatched. A few days before this the hen will start to communicate with her young by clucking, and this helps them all to hatch around the same time. Hen-hatched chicks appear to be healthier and more vigorous than artificially hatched chicks.

The last chicks to hatch may get stuck because the membrane is too dry. Some people spray the eggs with warm water in the last few days to prevent this. If hatchlings seem stuck you can try assisting them by enlarging the hole they' ve pipped in the egg and then sprinkling or spraying warm water over them. But often these chicks are the weaker ones that die anyhow.

Chicks that are ' dead in shell' , having died in the third week, could have died as a result of nutritional deficiencies in the parents and are often low in B vitamins. Best to concentrate on preventing such problems.

The chicks

Newly hatched chicks soon dry out and fluff up. They need little but warmth for the first day or so, while they wait for their siblings to emerge. They do not need food or water at first because they absorb the yolk just before hatching – although they do appreciate a shallow dish of water, especially in hot weather. This is why hatcheries can transport hatchlings over long distances without providing food and water.

If the hen gets off the nest before all the chicks have hatched, you can collect the remaining eggs and try to keep them warm. Another broody, a hot water bottle or an electric frypan on its lowest setting (with a damp towel beneath the eggs) may do the trick.

When these chicks hatch, wait until they are strong enough to join their older siblings before reintroducing them, at night, to their mum. As long as they are no more than a day or two old they should accept each other. If the hen does not accept the chicks she may peck them to death, so keep a close eye on them at first.

By about 6 weeks of age the chicks start to become independent and

Happy hen with healthy chickens. (There's nothing like having a real mother to teach you all about life!)

mother hen may even start to lay again, in which case she will soon lose all interest in the chicks.

How to feed chicks
Within a short time the new chicks will be wolfing down food. Feed them as much as they can eat in 5– 10 minutes. Lots of small feeds throughout the day are ideal, as the chicks' crops are very tiny. Put food on newspaper initially as it makes it easier for the chicks to eat – but watch the chicks don' t slip and slide as this can cripple them. Sawdust or corrugated cardboard can be a safer option.

Make sure the chicks can' t drown in the water containers either, by placing a little ramp or rock in the water. Check the chicks several times daily to see that feed and water containers are all right.

Chicks in a brooder
If you have obtained day-old chicks, or if something has happened to your mother hen, you may need to artificially rear your chicks. This need not be difficult, as you can put together a quick brooder box with household items. (But it is a poor substitute compared to a real mother!)

Get a good strong cardboard box, with plenty of space for all chicks. Put a layer of sawdust or clean sand in the bottom and this will later become a valuable resource for the compost heap. Now find an ordinary household lamp, with a 25 or 40 watt incandescent globe, and place it inside the box and turn it on. (Don' t use compact fluorescent bulbs, they generate radio frequency radiation.) Alternatively, suspend a light inside an upturned terracotta flowerpot placed in the box to radiate heat. Add feed dishes and shallow watering troughs that the chicks can' t get stuck in (a chill could kill), and the brooder is ready.

With artificial brooding the ideal temperature starts at 38°C when chicks are young and is reduced each week. It should be reduced to 20°C by the fifth week, by which time feathering should be complete.

To begin with, watch the chicks' behaviour to get the temperature right. If they huddle directly under the light it may be too cold for them. If they keep well away, it may be too hot.

A brooder box and heat lamp, inside an insulated shed.

As the chicks grow they need less external heat and will venture to cooler parts of the box. The chicks will be able to self-regulate the temperature of their environment by moving closer to and further away from the source of heat. If chicks can do this, there is no need to adjust the temperature, although you may need to raise or lower the light bulb, depending on changes in the weather.

The only problem with using a light in the brooder is that it makes the chicks a bit overactive, nervous and easily frightened. To avoid this you could paint the light bulb black, try the terracotta pot method, keep the chicks beside a slow combustion cooker or, in an emergency, make up a hot water bottle. Specialised heat lamps, which give out heat, but not light, are also available commercially.

The old idea of the hay-box can be employed, dispensing with heating altogether. (No worries if there' s a power failure!) Hay bales can be placed around the brooder box with some layers of hessian over the top. This should keep chicks cosy on a cold night, as it conserves all their body heat. Just ensure there is sufficient ventilation.

Lawn chicks

On a warm sunny day, when the chicks are a few weeks old, you can allow them to forage on a short lawn in a movable pen. If you move the pen every couple of days, the lawn will really benefit from the fertiliser and will become lush and thick. Of course, you will have to watch the weather!

One day a sudden cold, windy, rain squall descended on my farm. By the time I had dashed around the house, shutting windows and the like, my chicks, which had been sunbaking half an hour previously, were soaking wet and shivering.

I quickly popped the chicks into a plastic clothes basket and installed a hot fan in front of them. This dried them out within an hour, by which time they were panting with thirst and needed a long drink. So did I!

After 5 or 6 weeks chicks can happily go out into netted yards or coops, where they will soon learn the art of foraging. Keep the young pullets and cockerels in flocks of their own age group; otherwise older birds will bully them. It's best to rear them on clean ground – this will prevent them picking up intestinal worms and other health problems. Use land that has not had poultry on it for a year or more.

Predators

Beware of predators when young birds are free ranging. Rats and feral cats will take chicks, as will birds of prey including kookaburras, hawks, crows and magpies. Check your chicks several times a day.

If predators are a problem and playing ' mother goose' is not possible, you might find it beneficial to raise a puppy along with your young flock of chicks. The dog will bond as ' family' and, if the breed is appropriate, it will herd and guard the flock.

There are specific dog breeds for flock protection, the Italian Maremma being one. These big white gentle giants will live outdoors with the flock and be great defenders of it.

Vikki, my Jack Russell terrier (pictured below), treats all the fowl as family. She is gentle and motherly with little chicks, but cheeky with roosters and turkeys! She guards the birds against attacks by hawks, eagles, dogs and foxes. In fact, she regards many other animals as a threat to the flock. (Yet her father was a chicken killer!)

Joining me on feeding trips, she is constantly buzzing around hunting for rats. When asked to do so, Vikki will chase and catch birds with delight, holding them down by straddling over them until I arrive on the scene. But she never deliberately hurts them.

Vikki treats the poultry as her playmates, while rats and feral rabbits are hunted relentlessly and killed immediately. Her normal doggy behaviour has been modified, from a tender age, by intensive training and familiarisation with her feathered family.

Poultry Health – Naturally!

The maintenance of natural health and well-being is dependent on good feeding and management, and the use of preventative medicine.

Good management means no overcrowding, access to clean water, plenty of wholesome and varied fresh food (including green pick), sunshine as well as shade, exercise, quarantining of new birds, regular prophylactic (preventative) treatment with herbs, and the composting of deep litter to reduce the levels of parasites and harmful microbes.

Poultry living in unnatural, stressful conditions will easily succumb to disease. The factory farmer's response is to routinely add medication to feed and to use antibiotics as growth promotants.

The immune systems of naturally reared birds repel and fight off disease. Many of the old purebreds are renowned for this ability. They were never as intensively farmed as they are now and were selected for good disease resistance over the generations.

Ducks are fairly resistant to disease, although they can suffer from leg and eye problems. If one of your ducks is limping, isolate it and keep it confined to a small area to give its legs a rest. To reduce the incidence of eye infections, keep ducks' water clean at all times.

What to look out for
Check poultry daily to ascertain their state of health. At feeding times, particularly, observe their behaviour, appearance and vitality.

Sick birds often mope around on their own, lagging behind the rest. They will hunch their heads into their bodies, fluff out their feathers and let their tails droop. The birds' vents may also be soiled as diarrhoea is a common symptom of many health problems. Several sick birds may huddle together miserably.

Close observation is especially needed during spells of bad weather or stress. When birds look unhealthy, quick action is necessary.

Modern 'wisdom' advocates the killing of birds that are ill, because it takes too long to get them back to health, and that is uneconomical. This method of dealing with illness in poultry is also meant to stop the spread of contagious disease.

You don't have to subscribe to this belief. It is possible to keep poultry alive, nursing the birds back to health and giving herbal and homeopathic remedies to provide relief. A bit of compassion and good nursing can work wonders with sick poultry.

Generally speaking, acute problems are invariably assisted by homeopathic first aid, while slower acting herbal remedies can help more chronic problems. Helpful information can be found in many an old farm book; there is often a great deal of wisdom in them. It pays to double-check the information, however. Not all the old herbal remedies can be trusted!

'Remedies' to avoid

If you want to live naturally and avoid toxic chemicals, forget about remedies such as:

- creosote, which is used for painting around sheds to repel parasites although it is highly toxic
- stock tar products, which are used for treating skin problems
- sump oil, which is used for treating scaly leg and which is full of toxins that birds can ingest when cleaning themselves.

Tobacco is another nasty 'remedy' once commonly prescribed for poultry. I came across one sixty-year-old book that described the use of tobacco smoke to treat gapes (throat worms). The method was to ' *...put chicks in a covered box with a pan of live coals, onto which have been sprinkled fine cut tobacco. The chickens should be left in the box until they become drunk or stupefied but not long enough to smother them...This treatment never fails!'*

While it may be natural and will indeed kill worms, tobacco is much too deadly to pass organic standards. It really has no place in the garden or farm and is best totally avoided!

Common problems, nature's remedies

Parasitic worms and body lice are the most common problems affecting fowl. Ducks are affected to a lesser extent. Fortunately, there are a number of easily accessible herbs available to counter such pests. All of these herbs have multiple uses, with medicinal or tonic powers as well. Profiles of these plants are found in Chapter 8.

Worms

The eggs of roundworms thrive in shady places; hot weather destroys them, as does composting of litter. Tapeworms are spread by snails, slugs and insects, which eat their eggs. Heavy tapeworm infestations produce toxins that affect the nervous system, resulting in leg weakness. Fortunately, ducks are not affected by tapeworm and are, in fact, valuable predators of the tapeworms' hosts.

Symptoms of worm infestation

If worm infestations are severe, plumage may be loose and fluffed out, eyes dull and discharging, droppings blood stained and irregular, with 'dirty pants' evident. Birds may also display reduced appetite and increased thirst. They will often huddle up and appear lethargic. There will be weight loss, with pallor of comb and wattles.

Worm prevention

Ideally, of course, you need to treat for worms *before* birds develop such drastic symptoms. In fact, regular prophylactic treatment will prevent general demise, because birds may succumb to other problems when the worm load is high.

Never overstock! Poultry that is overstocked will be exposed to high levels of worm eggs on the ground from infested birds' droppings. Rotate birds regularly to fresh areas in order to rest the ground. Alternate them between two or more yards, or move them around in a mobile pen. Keep their homes clean and dry.

Nettles are a great worm preventative herb, as well as being good food for poultry. Boil the nettles in whey and administer the liquid when cold by adding it to mash. Or dry and powder it and sprinkle into mash.

Another traditional preventative is to give fresh or sour milk every morning, ideally unpasteurised. Don't give both; just keep to either fresh or sour. Half a litre of milk is sufficient for 10 adult fowl or 20 chickens. The birds will also benefit from the food value.

Worm treatments

According to ancient wisdom the best time to treat worms is when they are most active - when the moon is waxing full.

Garlic

Garlic is generally the preferred organic treatment for worm control. The recommended dose is 1 or 2 cloves per fowl.

A good way to give birds garlic is to make a cold extract by standing several cloves of crushed garlic in half a cup of water for 6- 8 hours. Use an eyedropper or teaspoon to administer the extract to each bird. Alternatively, place the garlic extract in the fowl's drinking vessels for several days in a row just before the full moon. Keep plain water away from them while using this method of administration.

Another method is to crush garlic cloves and put them in a stocking. Leave the stocking to hang in the fowls' water for a week. Use about 1kg of garlic per 50L of water. After a week's break, repeat the treatment. Repeat it again after 3 months.

You can also feed finely chopped garlic tops to your poultry. The birds will generally eat only what they need. Remember, however, that garlic is rich in sulphur; excessive garlic should not be given to hens that are laying, if you don' t want the smell to taint the eggs.

Anti-worm recipe

A mash to rid one average-sized fowl of worms can be made using:

   1 handful of wormwood and tansy tips

   1 leaf of comfrey

   1 cup of crushed oats or barley

   1 clove of crushed garlic

   Water

Chop up the wormwood and tansy tips, and the comfrey leaf. Add the chopped leaves and a clove of crushed garlic to a cup of crushed oats or barley. Mix with a little water to make a gluggy porridge and feed the mixture as the only food every second day, for 3 days. Give a little grain on alternate days.[1]

The amounts specified will make enough mash to treat one fowl. Increase amounts for extra birds.

Other herbal remedies

Alternatively, or additionally, you can add finely chopped anti-worm herbs to the fowl's feed on a regular basis – every full moon, say. The birds will eat only what they need, however, as a starting point the herbs should make up about 20% of the ration.

Anti-worm herbs and foods include:

• the leaves of horseradish, garlic, elder, cotton-lavender, rue (fresh or dried in small amounts), hyssop, goat's rue, bramble, Pacific coral tree and white cedar

• onions

• grated or cooked carrot

• wormwood tips, or dried and powdered flowering wormwood tops

• tansy flowers and seeds

• ground up mustard, carrot, fennel or pumpkin seeds.

Nasturtium seeds are also a good wormer, as well as having a tonic, antiseptic and medicinal action. The birds will eat only what they need so you can experiment to determine how much is needed: observe amounts left over and adjust rations accordingly. The seeds can be preserved in vinegar. In fact, a little apple cider vinegar in the drinking water will also help repel worms.

Wormy birds that are not already weak or quite sick can be put on a short fast and then a laxative diet. Senna is a herb used for purging after a fast. A popular laxative, senna helps restore the digestive system. Steep 1.5 pods per hen in cold water for 4 hours. Add a good pinch of powdered ginger to help disinfection and to reduce the griping caused by senna.

With many of these potent herbs it is important to be aware that they can be toxic if ingested in large quantities - so don' t overdose. But with sufficient free choice feeding allowed, birds will probably self-medicate from herbal mixtures on offer and take only what is needed.

Lice, mites, ticks and fleas
These external parasites are a common poultry problem. The tiny pests love to hide on the birds' warm, moist bodies, either eating protein-rich feathers or sucking blood. Lice are more abundant on unhealthy or stressed birds, and on battery farm hens that have had their beaks trimmed. They can cause a lot of irritation and misery. They can even jump onto you and cause irritation!

Lice are more prevalent in the cold time of year and don't suck blood. Mites, on the other hand, breed up in the warmer months and do suck blood. In Australia there are two main mite species, the red and the tropical. Red mites attack at night, then hide in the night house by day. The tropical mite stays on the bird most of the time. Ticks and fleas also suck blood.

Poultry will keep pest levels down, especially ticks, to some extent by preening each other and by rolling around in dustbaths. But when weather is wet for long spells and dustbaths get damp, pest numbers can rapidly increase.

Symptoms of infestation
If lice are not treated, sore, bare skin patches and eczema-like areas
develop. Broody hens will leave the nest if untreated. You'll know mites
are present when you inspect the egg settings and see tiny black dots
moving over the eggs. Check the feathers around the vent and under
the wings for signs of lice.

Preventative measures
Sulphur, a naturally occurring mineral, is an old remedy for deterring
sucking insects such as fleas, ticks and mites. It can be taken internally
or used as a fumigant. If powdered and mixed into a special mash, it can
be fed to poultry at monthly intervals, in combination with worming
and tonic herbs. Sulphur is toxic to many beneficial organisms, so care
must be taken in its use. But it is acceptable under organic standards.

Aromatic tree branches such as camphor laurel if used as perches will
help repel lice. Neem tree leaves placed in the nest will do likewise.
Bracken can also be used as a nest lining as it repels many insect pests.

Grow insecticidal plants near the fowl house for a permanent deterrent
effect. You can also cover the fowl shed floor with sawdust and
shavings from camphor laurel, oregon or other aromatic timbers.

Treatments
A pinch of sulphur per bird in feed on a regular basis will make fowl
less prone to parasite infestation of any sort. Garlic is rich in sulphur
and 1 or 2 cloves per bird in drinking water also reduces the risk of
parasite infestation. Sulphur can be given in homeopathic form, too.

External treatments can involve insecticidal powder, herbal brew (eg a
10% solution of garlic extract) or spray applied directly onto infestations
of lice, ticks, fleas or mites. Apply while holding birds upside down by
the legs, over a sheet of newspaper to catch the powder. When dusting
or spraying, pay particular attention to the areas under wings and
around the vent. Repeat after a week or two. If spraying, do so only on
a warm, sunny day, or birds may get chilled.

You can also try dusting birds with dry wood ash, or with dried and powdered aromatic herbs, such as rosemary mixed with equal parts of wormwood - a good combination.

Commercial products include derris dust or rotenone powder. (It's good to wear a dust mask when applying these.) Pyrethrum based products or quassia solution can also be sprayed.

Neem tree products can be useful. If used regularly, neem oil and kernel extract are effective in the control and prevention of many pests.

Anti-parasite recipe
Marja Fitzgerald's anti-parasite recipe calls for:

Two thirds cup of bran or pollard per bird
1 level teaspoon of sulphur per two birds
1 tablespoon of molasses per two birds
1 clove of crushed garlic per bird
1 teaspoon of seaweed meal per five birds
1 tablespoon of apple cider vinegar per five birds
1 teapoon dolomite per bird [2]

Mix all the ingredients together, except the garlic and vinegar, and add very hot water. Leave the mixture to stand for 2 hours. When cool, add the garlic and apple cider vinegar. The mixture makes a wonderfully healthy meal that is best given when the moon is full.

Insecticidal herbs
There are many multi-purpose backyard herbs that can be used to repel insects. Among the best are wormwood, southernwood, mugwort, tansy, stinking roger, rosemary, catnip, feverfew, rue, peppermint and lemongrass.

Other herbal remedies specific to lice include alder bark decoction in vinegar, aniseed salve, crushed columbine seeds, pennyroyal, larkspur seed tincture, parsley and angelica fruit.

Insecticidal herbs can be used in several ways. You can:
- grow the herbs inside the poultry run so that the birds can nibble them and brush against them
- add dried or powdered herbs to the birds' feed
- rub powdered herbs into the birds' feathers
- make the herbs into a strong brew with which to wash the birds
- crush or burn herbs and strew them around the hen house.

To make an insecticidal herb brew - place the freshly collected herb (about 1 handful per bird should do) in water and simmer for 3 minutes. Cool the liquid, then bottle it (with the herb left in it), and keep it in a cool, dark place until you are ready to use it.

Insecticidal oils
Oils have been used for insect control since ancient times. Popular household deodorisers, they used to be burnt in a vapouriser.

Herbal essential oils containing cineole (eucalpytus being pre-eminent) and terpines (which resemble oil of turpentine –   a traditional insect repellant) are used as medicines and insecticides; while those rich in citral and citronella are mostly used for perfumes, fungicides and flavouring, as well as insecticides.

Certain oils have particular repellant properties:
- eucalpytus oil is excellent against bacteria, fungi, insects and mites
- lavender oil is a powerful general insect repellent
- citronella (lemongrass) oil controls mosquitoes
- tea tree oil is antifungal, antibacterial and a general insect repellent
- lemon grass oil deters most flying insects
- thyme oil repels hopping and crawling insects
- sassafrax oil repels lice
- camphor oil keeps away moths
- scented geranium oil is a good general pest repellant
- pennyroyal, catnip, spearmint and peppermint –   the oil-rich foliage of these plants can be used to repel rodents and parasites.

Trees and shrubs with aromatic oils often have insecticidal properties that can also be employed in several ways. You can plant them around fowl houses and where they will be brushed against or perched in.

Alternatively, you can process the leaves by soaking or boiling them to release the essential oils. Half fill a small bucket with the aromatic leaves and pour in enough boiling water to cover them. This should make sufficient liquid to spray around an average size fowl house.

Commercial grade essential oils for spraying can be diluted at 15 drops in about 50ml of water. Leaves rich in aromatic oils can also be used as bedding or mulch that will repel parasites. Chopped up leaves release oils over a period of time and can be regularly topped up as permanent protection.

You can chop up a big pile of leaves easily by either putting it through a mulcher or running the lawn mower over it several times.

The dustbath

A bird's daily dustbath is a natural means of lice control. Try to make sure that your birds' dustbathing area is sheltered from rain and free from run-off.

In the event of a bad lice infestation you can help birds by adding repellents to the dustbath on a weekly basis. Use either:

- derris dust or rotenone powder
- powdered quassia chips
- crushed charcoal or coal cinders
- the dried leaves of bamboo, white cedar or neem trees
- diatomaceous earth, dolomite or lime
- dried and powdered herbs such as wormwood, southernwood lavender, hyssop, pennyroyal, tansy, peppermint or pyrethrum.

House hygiene

Lice, ticks and mites hide in the cracks and crevices of fowl houses.

You can zap these insects with an insecticidal spray made from simple household ingredients such as:
- equal parts kerosene and water; or
- water, soap and paraffin.

Mix the ingredients together while they are boiling, then squirt the mixture everywhere while it is still very hot. Repeat in 4 or 5 days.

Pouring liquid paraffin into cracks and crevices is an old trick. So is whitewashing walls, perches and crevices with lime. Whitewashing should be repeated in 2 weeks; while liming of floors is also good.

Peoples' houses were once fumigated by burning juniper and cedar wood. The so-called strewing herbs, such as cayenne pepper, could be used to fumigate fowl sheds but this will only work if you can make the shed airtight.

Modern organic poultry producers often disinfect sheds by spraying them with tea tree oil, diluted 1:100 (half teaspoon oil to 1 cup water).

Scaly leg
Looking like a white crusty leg deformity, scaly leg is caused by a build-up of scabies-like mites that burrow under skin. The condition is extremely irritating and can lead to lameness in fowl.

To get at the mites, start by soaking the affected fowl's legs in very soapy water that has a little ammonia added. Gently scrub the white crust with a nailbrush. This aids penetration of insecticidal substances.

Then apply any of the following mixtures to the fowl's legs:
- a brew of half garlic and half vinegar, plus a pinch of cayenne.
- vaseline and sulphur, 200g to 1 tablespoon (heat and mix);[3] or vaseline alone (mites won't be able to breathe under the Vaseline); or a proprietary vaseline-based chest rub
- kerosene and raw linseed oil in equal parts[4]
- cheap cooking oil, with a few drops of kerosene or tea tree, eucalyptus or sassafrax oil added
- cooking oil with an equal amount of crushed white cedar flowers soaked in it for several hours
- neem extract spray
- commercial herbal lotion for human head lice (dilute with oil)
- aloe vera pulp blended with some water and olive oil plus a few drops tea tree oil (made thick enough not to fall off)[7]

You can also skip the scrubbing process, if you prefer, and just use the remedies prescribed above. Apply treatments several times until the crusty exudate and old scales fall off.

While you' re about it, it' s a good idea to clear out pens and spray perches with insecticidal brew as old scabs and scales from infested birds stay infective for 30 days.

Health disorders

The nasty diseases that sometimes affect intensive poultry farms are often symptomatic of unhealthy living conditions. They are less common in the backyard situation. With good management your birds should stay healthy. However, you must always keep a close eye on their appearance and behaviour for problem signs.

There are several bacterial and viral diseases of poultry that are not described here: they are rarely encountered in the backyard or free-range situation. The prophylactic use of herbs and the presence of healthy bacteria in deep litter will enhance your birds' natural resistance to all disease.

The best advice I can give is don't wait until your birds get sick, then panic! Discover which poultry herbs grow best in your area and start planting! Birds will self-medicate if appropriate herbs are available to them. And keep a few common medications in the first aid box, too.

Diarrhoea

Sometimes called 'dirty pants', diarrhoea is a common symptom of many conditions such as digestive upsets, enteritis and worms. It' s fostered by dirty conditions or food. The most likely cause of diarrhoea in chicks is coccidiosis.

To treat diarrhoea, give a half teaspoon of slippery elm powder to ease inflamed intestines, to which you might add a similar amount of yoghurt, yoghurt powder or brewer' s yeast. Make the mixture into a slurry by adding water and pour it down the bird's throat using a teaspoon. Dill and powdered charcoal can also be given; as can a half teaspoon of Epsom Salts per bird added to feed.[5]

For affected chicks, try feeding a diet of either boiled rice with honey and milk; or cooked arrowroot, grated raw apples, and fresh or dry bilberries. Also wheat bran moistened with sour or butter milk is good.

Routine garlic in the birds' drinking water once a week is a good preventative, at one clove per bird. (Garlic can also be bought in powdered form and sprinkled in food.)

Poisoning

Common poisoning symptoms include moping, ruffled feathers, thirst, diarrhoea, convulsions, loss of mobility, paralysis and sudden death.

Poisonous plants include hemlock, lily of the valley, rhubarb leaves, black locust leaves and potato sprouts or peel that is going green.

Other poisonous plants include:
- the mother of millions plant, which contains a cardiac toxin
- amaranth – the raw seed is hepatoxic (it requires heat treatment)
- Chilean or green cestrum, a pungent weed with yellow tubular flowers and oval black berries, looking similar to black nightshade
- petty spurge, a native of Europe and Asia and widespread weed of cultivation in Australia, which causes loss of appetite and egg laying capacity in fowls
- inkweed, also called pokeroot, which grows to 2m and has red stems, and purple black berries that have purgative, narcotic and irritant properties, causing internal and skin ailments in poultry
- crotalaria, a green manure legume that is considered poisonous to livestock and poultry
- whorled milkweed, also considered poisonous to poultry.

Sometimes feedstuffs that are old or damp grow poisonous mycotoxins (moulds). Always check feed before giving it out. And never put wet mash into feed troughs where old mash remains. Clean troughs thoroughly first. Ingested moulds cause birds to become listless, lose their appetite and die within a couple of weeks. Birds may also suffer respiratory distress with rapid breathing from inhaling aspergillus moulds such as those found in hay.

Botulism

Botulism is a very nasty, although uncommon, bacterial infection generally caused by birds consuming rotten food or drinking filthy water. The distinguishing symptoms are 'limber neck' (the bird being unable to raise its head), diarrhoea and wasting away. Sick birds are usually culled, or killed, and the site disinfected, but careful nursing may save the bird.

Try giving a teaspoon of Epsom salts per bird (mix with a littel water and pour down the throat); or a 14ml dose of castor oil every few days. Or try a drop of oregano oil plus cinnamon powder or oil added to feed.

Colds

Fasting followed by a laxative diet can help. The daily dietary addition of garlic, and chopped onion and mustard greens is helpful. Teaspoons of strong sage tea can be given, along with inhalations of eucalyptus vapour. Horseradish pills can also be given. Keep birds warm, and give finely chopped chilli or pepper in food to help heat them.

Coccidiosis

This protozoan disease is usually only a problem where stocking density is excessive, such as in a commercial situation. Warmth and damp also foster the disease.

Symptoms of coccidiosis include blood-stained, runny white droppings, head and wings flopping down, mournful cheeping and the lethargic victims wasting away.

Chicks are prone to getting coccidiosis and that is why coccidiostat drugs are routinely put into commercial chicken feed. There can be up to 90% mortality, however chicks reared by a hen are seldom affected.

Good management and hygiene, a balanced diet, no overcrowding and a dry environment, plus feedstuffs (such as gotu kola) that contain high levels of vitamin K and A are the best preventative. Yoghurt and buttermilk will help, as will dried skim milk added to mash (40% of volume). Whey powder, at 10% of feed, is also a good preventative that can be fed routinely to chicks between 4 and 8 weeks of age.

During an outbreak of the disease, make sure chicks get plenty of water. Feed them plenty of finely chopped greens, especially comfrey, parsley, aloe vera, onions, gotu kola or ginger. Garlic (of course!) does wonders. Half a teaspoon of slippery elm powder per bird will reduce the diarrhoea. Add water to the powder and pour the slurry down the affected birds' throats using a teaspoon.

Coccidiosis eggs, or oocytes, are destroyed by dry or frosty conditions, so moving the birds to clean land reduces the risk of continued exposure to the disease.

Exposure to low levels of oocytes helps build immunity (adults rarely succumb), so some exposure is good. In fact, if you allow deep litter in the night house to build up and manage it as you would a healthy compost heap, the pathogenic microorganisms will be kept in check by the non-pathogenic ones.

Properly managed deep litter helps keep both coccidiosis and salmonella at bay. However, it can lead to a worm egg build-up, so you must remove deep litter regularly and finish it off by hot composting in a heap, moistening and turning it a few times. Always leave some of the old litter as a bacterial starter for the new. Mortality rates can drop by as much as a third with well-managed deep litter, compared to using only fresh litter.

Marek's disease

This is a herpes-type viral disease, which attacks the nerves and causes tumours. It affects chickens from 6 weeks of age.

Symptoms include dropped wings and legs paralysed in a straddled position. However, birds may die suddenly with no symptoms at all in an acute attack. The disease spreads slowly and little can be done when a bird succumbs.

Exposure to Marek's disease may result in 10– 30% of chicks developing the disease, although if exposed to a particularly virulent strain up to 80% may develop the disease. Some strains of fowl are more resistant than others, the game fowl, for example. Barnevelders are quite susceptible. In commercial establishments all birds are vaccinated against Marek's disease. Breeding from unaffected birds with natural resistance is recommended.

Marek's disease is passed on from the mother and from feather particles in dust. If you suspect your hens are infected with Marek's disease it is best to hatch any eggs in an incubator, rather than let hens sit on them. Wipe the eggs with a cloth dampened with a disinfecting agent before putting them in the incubator. Parasites and insects can also spread the disease.

Sometimes the following conditions can be confused with Marek's disease: worms, especially tapeworm and round worm; coccidiosis, leucosis complex (affecting older birds, it rarely shows paralytic symptoms); infectious arthritis and bumblefoot (where a puncture wound leads to a staphylococcal infection).

Fowl pox

The fowl pox virus comes in two different forms and is generally spread by mosquitoes and via wounds or scratches. The most common form is when wart-like lesions and scabs develop on the face.

The form known as diphtheria involves the mouth and throat, with a cheesy substance growing there (which may eventually cause suffocation). The nostrils may also become affected, swelling and producing a runny discharge. Birds may be depressed, lose their appetite and have greenish diarrhoea. Fowl pox used to be known as roup, and diphtheria as canker.

Treatments involve a bit of 'TLC', or tender loving care, so most books recommend culling affected birds and vaccinating the remainder! However, birds *can* recover and they will have lifelong immunity afterwards, unlike the immunity imparted by vaccination. The natural course of the virus lasts a couple of weeks.

A natural remedy is to give garlic internally, 1– 2 cloves per bird in food, and externally, as a lotion on the scabs. Iodine solution can also be dabbed on the lesions. Vitamins A, C and E can be given in water

ily. Bairacli Levy recommends giving birds a couple of drops of
ıcalyptus oil daily (one drop per dose). Administer the (diluted) drops
ally using a pen filler.[6]

ıseline can be used to stop the eyelids from sticking together and you
n remove the cheesy substance from the throat, mouth and nostrils
ing tweezers. A drop of eucalyptus oil in the bird's nostrils can help if
ere is copious discharge.

ew herbal fowl pox cure

*ben fowl pox broke out in my flock for the first time, I
perimented with an ointment made from the herb gotu kola
escribed in Chapter 8), plus drops used internally. I daubed the
rds' faces twice a day with the green lotion and, using an
edropper, squirted diluted gotu kola juice down their throats.*

*ter 3 days of treatment, the lesions had shrunk, then the infectious
ıbs proceeded to drop off. After a few more days of quarantine they
ʾre put back with the flock. I have subsequently repeated this
ccess using the same regime on other affected birds.*

make a cold extract with gotu kola, use one leaf per bird per day.
ıop leaves finely, grind them in a mortar and pestle, then strain out
₂ juice. Fresh juice diluted with water can be administered using an
edropper, or you can add the juice to the drinking water.

r a healing lotion for external use, mix the fresh juice of gotu kola
th something like a plain lanolin hand cream. Use enough juice to
ike the resultant cream pale green.

atural first aid for birds
ɔunds
r open wounds, Calendula tincture is an excellent wash. Made from
rigolds, Calendula is very cleansing and soothing, and can also be
ed for burns. A mixture of half Calendula and half Hypericum tincture
ılso an excellent wash. Hypericum being good for puncture wounds.
dab gential violet onto the wound, followed by minced aloe vera. [7]

Sometimes wounds become infected and boils develop. These may need to be lanced at the base, then dabbed with a disinfecting agent.

Broken leg
Fowl's legs are fairly strong and can be grabbed when catching them. Not so ducks, who more easily suffer leg injuries.

If one of your birds suffers a broken leg a splint can be made using elder wood, or a stout feather if it is a chick. Keep the splint in place with a strip of old nylon pantyhose and some sticking plaster.

You can also stand the leg in comfrey brew thrice daily and give a teaspoon of comfrey brew internally at the same time.

Egg bound
Sometimes a hen makes obvious attempts to lay, but nothing happens and she exhibits signs of distress. A warm bath and a little castor oil down the throat can be good to get the egg out. Or you could lubricate the vent with olive oil. Give the hen raspberry leaf tea to drink - it' s a great general tonic for layers and can also assist a hen to pass an egg. [8]

Callous / Bumblefoot
A callous on the foot may respond to having Tiger Balm or other warming essential oils massaged into it. If it' s an infected wound, first soak the foot clean in an Epsom salts solution, dab with Calendula tincture, then wrap in gauze, renewing the dressing twice daily until better. Or treat with aloe vera pulp blended with some water and olive oil plus a few drops of tea tree oil (made thick enough not to fall off). [7]

Cropbound
Sometimes items such as string or long grass can become lodged in the crop, which will remain distended and feel hard. Such crop impaction can cause death. A lubricant poured down the throat plus massage may help to fix the problem.

Give 1- 2 teaspoons of olive, castor, linseed or other vegetable oil, to which may be added 1 tablespoon of warm water. Then hold the bird's head down and gently knead the crop until the contents soften. Repeat in a couple of hours and gradually work the food down out of the crop. If all this fails, surgery may be required.

Health with homeopathy

Homeopathy is an exacting science and there are thousands of remedies to choose from. Homeopathic medicines are highly diluted and work on the principle that 'like cures like'. A substance that produces symptoms of disease in large doses is used in highly diluted form to treat similar symptoms. The greater the dilution, the greater the curative effect. For instance Arsenicum album, which causes vomiting and diarrhoea, is used homeopathically for food poisoning.

Homeopathy is older than our modern allopathic health system. But it certainly isn't out-dated. German physician Samuel Hahnemann devised and developed the system in the 18th century. Homeopathic doctors treat the English royal family and members of the royal family have been patrons of large homeopathic hospitals in the UK. But now in the 21st century it has reduced popularity and availability worldwide, having been denigrated by rival pharmaceutical companies.

Despite being said to merely provide placebo effects, the remedies work a treat on animals. Many poultry diseases can be treated with homeopathy, there are several useful books available and one can purchase specific remedy combinations for veterinary use.

First aid with homeopathy

There are many general remedies worth keeping in your medicine cabinet for first aid purposes, for both poultry and their keepers.

Arnica is a general panacea and first aid remedy that every householder should stock. Made from the small daisy Arnica montana, this remedy is indicated whenever there is shock, haemorrhage, dislocations, fractures, strains and sprains, any accident or trauma, bites, bruises of any kind, fright and limb paralysis.

After a stray dog had killed several of my ducks, I found a mauled survivor. Ducks are nervous creatures and can easily die from shock. I quickly put the duck in a dark, warm box to calm down and administered the remedy, Arnica, putting a couple of drops into her nostrils, holding her head up high. She made a complete recovery.

Rescue remedy has similar usage, being excellent for accidents, fright and shock. Gelsemium is indicated for 'shaking with fright' (as well as fever and influenza). Aconite is useful, too, for cases of shock or fright, accidents or injuries, plus acute fever and influenza, burns and bleeding.

Chamomilla is made from the wild chamomile plant, popular as a soothing herb tea. Chamomilla is useful for all types of pain (it's a classic teething remedy for babies, too). Hypericum also eases pain, particularly after bites and other painful blows and wounds.

Nervous temperaments and conditions can be soothed by remedies such as Scutellaria, made from a member of the mint family. It is an excellent 'nerve' remedy, almost a tranquiliser.

The bird that is depressed or pining may well respond to Pulsatilla, a remedy made from European buttercup, or pasque flower. Ignatia is also good for treating grief.

An Asian tree known as poison-nut, the seeds of which contain strychnine and brucine, is the source of the remedy Nux Vomica. This treats chronic conditions of colic, digestive upsets and loss of appetite. Arsenicum is excellent in cases of acute vomiting and diarrhoea, and is also used to treat some chronic skin conditions.

To administer a homeopathic remedy it needs to be absorbed by an animal' s mucous membranes. The easiest way its to hold the bird firmly with head tilted upwards and put a drop or 2 into one of its nostrils.

Sometimes a remedy will not work until you have obtained the appropriate potency (dilution) of it. When you have the right potency, animals respond very well to treatment.

Another thing to be aware of in homeopathic treatment is the capacity of a remedy to cause aggravation of the condition. This worsening is only temporary and is not a cause for alarm. However you should stop giving treatment for 24 hours, or consult a homoeopath if it continues.

ually such a flare-up is followed by a complete removal of symptoms.

ιe beauty of homeopathic treatment is that it is low cost, non-toxic,
sy to use, and has no serious side effects.

st the thing for natural poultry care!

dnotes

Healy, P. 1988, ' Poultry the Organic Way' , *Growing Today*, Spring, p. 3.

Fitzgerald, M.1998, pers. comm., 14 Jan.

Marold, L. 1995, *Chookwise*, L. Marold, Castlemaine, Australia, p. 33.

James, Dr. T. 1994, ' Scaly Leg in Poultry' , *Australasian Poultry*, April– May, vol. 5,
no. 1, p. 28.

Earnest, P., *Chicken Diseases & Treatment*, Mother Earth News USA 1974 (online).

Bairacli Levy, Juliette de, 1976, *Herbal Handbook for Farm and Stable*, Rodale
Press, United States of America, p. 252.

http://www.countryfarm-lifestyles.com/natural-home-remedies-for-sick-chickens.html

http://www.birdchannel.com/bird-magazines/bird-talk/2011-march/tea-time.aspx

Poultry and Permaculture

Backyard food production is one way in which people can reduce their environmental impact on the Earth, improve their health and save money at the same time. Poultry are excellent for integrating with vegetable and fruit production. In fact, in permaculture design poultry are viewed as ideal livestock for an edible landscape.

If you do get to enjoy permaculture eggs from your own backyard, you can rest assured that this is the most ethical production system yet devised, although there is nothing new about the natural methods employed.

What is permaculture?
The word ' permaculture' stems from the concept of ' permanent culture' . Permanently sustaining cultures once enjoyed thousands of years of peaceful development. Their time-honoured agricultural systems worked in harmony with nature.

In contrast, modern monocultural farming destroys nature with chemicals and drains fertility. Land rendered unusable as a result of poison, salinity, erosion or exhaustion is often then abandoned to the processes of desertification. Intensive livestock operations may dump excessive fertiliser loads into the soil, burning off vegetation and contributing to toxic algal blooms in waterways. Quietly and insidiously, such land degradation is eating away at the planet.

Tasmanian Bill Mollison coined the term ' permaculture' while searching for a positive antidote to global environmental degradation. Formerly a CSIRO scientist, Mollison took up teaching at the University of Tasmania in 1968. By 1974, Mollison and his student David Holmgren had jointly evolved a conceptual framework for a sustainable agricultural system.[1]

Originally aimed at food self-sufficiency for households, permaculture has now grown to embrace appropriate legal, financial, business, housing and land sharing strategies, plus regional self-reliance. Basically, however, permaculture is about appropriate and sustainable design. In 1981, Bill taught the first graduates of a standard permaculture design course. Nowadays there are thousands of such graduates globally.

Permaculture design mimics nature – the ultimate role model. It is all about creating appropriate and productive ecosystems to suit individual sites. All parts of an ecosystem are connected in some way and permaculture makes use of those connections. Promoting practical ecology, biodiversity and the use of appropriate technology and energy efficiency to achieve sustainability, permaculture is common sense planning for the future.

A subtropical permaculture food forest featuring banana, paw paw, arrowroot and sweet potato, created by Bill Mollison at Tyalgum, northern New South Wales.

Permaculturists aim to eventually eliminate most external garden or farm inputs. Composting of any ' wastes' , for instance, ensures a continuous return of beneficial nutrients to the soil. Stock are rotated through pastures and yards where annual vegetables and tree crops are grown. This can eliminate the expense and work of buying and spreading fertiliser and pest control agents.

Fowl, for example, can greatly reduce codling moths, a serious pest in orchards, by scratching up and eating pupae when they overwinter in soil. When kept with cows, fowl will also reduce tick levels; while ducks eat many of the flies that bother cows. Ducks are also useful for liver fluke control when kept with ruminant stock as they eat the snails that host this fatal pest. Such multi-functionality is a cornerstone of good permaculture design.

The backyard food forest

Imagine yourself in a lush verdant forest, under fruit trees tangled in choko and bean vines, and seed-laden shrubs. Berries, native fruits and herbs fill the cool understorey zones beneath the trees. Yellow nodding sunflowers enjoy the sun on the forest edges. Underfoot, a dense soil-protecting carpet of sweet potato plants survive the scratching of busy, free-ranging fowl who gorge on fallen paw paws and other delights.

The backyard food forest, or permaculture orchard, is the ultimate habitat for poultry. Here fruit, vegetables, grasses, seeds, medicinal herbs and insects can be foraged at will by people and poultry. Valuable poultry manure is deposited directly where it' s needed and few external inputs are necessary in this perennially sustaining production system. It' s a permaculture paradise!

The classic natural forest blueprint maximises biological diversity to a point where pests and disease become less common. Insects become confused by the diversity of plants while native birds, their predators, are encouraged. Such a balanced ecology means that there is an equilibrium between plants and animals. Plants are ' stacked' vertically to maximise space. It' s an intensively productive ecosystem.

Establishing a food forest

In order to establish a backyard food forest, you must think in terms of planting a complete forest culture. Plant clumped plant groupings that combine a major fruit or nut tree; short-lived perennial legume shrubs; smaller shrubs such as berries; a lower layer of herbs, grasses or vegetables; and edible vines that climb the trees.

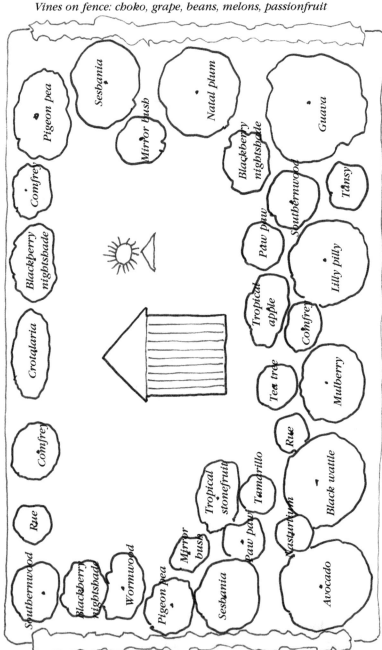

Vines on fence: choko, grape, beans, melons, passionfruit

Low plants this side

Taller trees this side

Vines on fence: choko, grape, beans, melons, passionfruit

Sample planting design for a permaculture poultry yard in a warm area, a mixture of fruiting and leguminous plants, plus shrubs, herbs and vines.

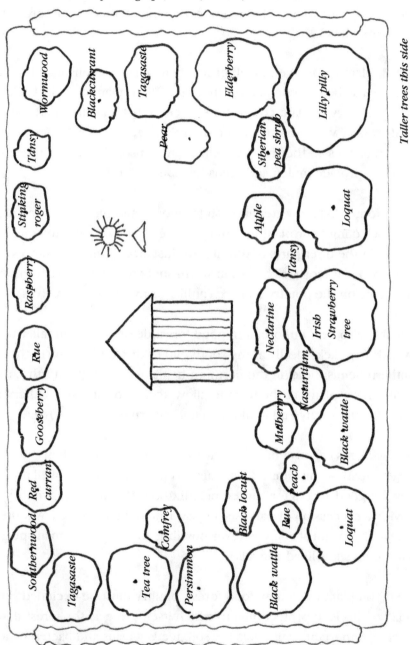

Vines on fence: grape, beans, berries, melons etc.

Low plants this side

Taller trees this side

Wormwood

Blackcurrant

Tagasaste

Elderberry

Lilly pilly

Tansy

Pear

Siberian pea shrub

Stinking roger

Apple

Loquat

Raspberry

Tansy

Rue

Nectarine

Irish Strawberry tree

Gooseberry

Nasturtium

Mulberry

Black wattle

Red currant

Peach

Southernwood

Comfrey

Rue

Loquat

Tagasaste

Tea tree

Persimmon

Black locust

Black wattle

Vines on fence: grape, beans, berries, melons

Sample planting design for a permaculture poultry yard in a temperate area.
Note that trees should not be planted too close to the fences as fowl could
use the trees as escape routes.

In this way your backyard food forest will mimic the natural forest, with its multiple levels.

Certain plants grow well together in a beneficial relationship, and are described as being ' companion species' . When planting your backyard food forest, try to plant companion species together. Plant herbs such as comfrey near your fruit trees, and interplant legume shrubs between the main fruit trees – they are not demanding on soil fertility, are short-lived and provide mulch and seeds for poultry food.

Don' t forget to take water and soil fertility requirements into account when selecting your plant groupings, either. Plant drought-tolerant species in the drier parts of the site, for instance. Fruiting rainforest plants will suit moist, rich soils in warm sheltered locations and they will thrive on the poultry manure (unlike many Australian natives).

Height is also very important in good forest design. Position taller trees towards the back, ideally at the south end of the food forest (in the southern hemisphere; in the northern hemisphere - to the north), and place smaller plants at the front to allow access to sunshine. Otherwise plants for the sunny end could be regularly pruned to stay lower.

Smaller plants can also be positioned on the edges. Here they enjoy ' edge effect' – maximised sun, air and rain exposure; as well as allowing good access for harvesting. Mixtures of plants that would provide a succession of harvests all year round are preferred. Another permaculture ' must' is, wherever possible, to select perennial species rather than short-lived annuals.

When you plant out a new food forest, poultry must be excluded initially. This is to protect mulch, which itself protects the forest floor. Mulch is important, as it cools the soil, feeds worms and bacteria and reduces moisture loss. Eventually, live ground-cover plants are established to replace the mulch and provide pickings for fowl. These include perennial herbs, grasses and grains. A packet of parrot seed will produce a good mixed crop in a sunny spot.

Hens enjoy their food forest home. Note the tree tomatoes and comfrey plants in the foreground.

Poultry should not be introduced until after ground covers have established. Young trees may require tree guards or heavy, rough mulch around them for a few years to keep poultry off the root zone.

Selecting forage plants

Forage plants in poultry yards can have a hard life! Excess nutrients and compaction will stress plants, which may then die. If you only select the hardiest of plants to begin with you will have fewer problems.

The following plants are ideally suited for poultry forage in a permaculture food forest. The list is not exhaustive and there are many other plants which poultry will eat. The plants listed are fairly common in Australia, and are safe, nutritious and palatable for poultry to eat in the raw state. Many of these plants are profiled in the next chapter.

Fruit trees and shrubs

Many varieties of fruit tree can provide windfall fruit that poultry will eagerly devour. In fact, citrus is probably the only fruit not eaten by poultry. If fruit are blown with fruit fly or some other pest - no worries! The extra protein will be appreciated by the birds. Elderberry, mulberry, persimmon and paw paw are excellent poultry forage.

Fruiting shrubs, such as gooseberries and other berries, mirror bush, blackberry nightshade and cotoneaster, provide tasty fruit when planted on the food forest edges.

Shade-tolerant fruiting plants can be selected for the shady understorey zone beneath trees.

Vines
Vines can provide good poultry forage when trailing in the food forest, or trained along fences. There are many to select from: grape, passionfruit, choko, cane fruit, some beans and peas, melons, cucumber and Virginia creeper.

Banana passionfruit is the most cold tolerant of the passionfruit family. It can be planted at the drip line of the tree it is to trail up. Kudzu is a rampant tropical woody legume that provides green pick and seeds until late in autumn. (It also has a bad reputation for weed potential.)

'Bush tucker'
Fruiting Australian rainforest ' bush tucker' plants are well suited to a food forest. Many are shade tolerant to some degree and belong in the understorey zone – Davidson' s plum is a good example.

Sunloving species include the lilly pilly, native figs, crab apple, native mulberry, kangaroo apple and Burdekin plum. Some of these native plants have commercial potential and will also provide food for wildlife.

There are many species of native vines and climbing berry bushes that would be worth trying, such as the various native grapes, apple-berries and the molucca bramble. Such species provide good poultry forage. Not only that, bush tucker is in big demand by specialty restaurants and bushfood supply companies, so you may make some money from the produce.

Ground covers and herbs
Ground covers are necessary in the food forest. They keep soil cool and moist, and protect it from poultry scratching and erosion.

Useful species, many of which are thought of as mere weeds, include:
- pigweed (Portulacca)
- chickweed
- wandering jew (Tradescantia)
- fat hen
- shepherd' s purse (which is said to stimulate egg production)
- sow-thistle
- cleavers (rich in iron and iodine)
- plantain (loved by ducks)

Soya bean plants provide good green pick and thrive on land too acid for clover or alfalfa.

Comfrey is a high-protein perennial herb growing to 1m and dying back each winter in cold parts. It is also an excellent companion to fruit trees and will keep weeds at bay if grown beneath them.

Sweet potato is a tough ground cover for warm areas, its tubers and cooked stems and leaves providing food for people and green pick for poultry.

A comfrey border along a permaculture hen run is a good weed suppressant.

Vegetable greens to grow around the food forest include silver beet, chard, cabbage, chou moellier (a tall loose-leaf cabbage), dandelion, endive, lamb's lettuce, Chinese greens, salsify and rocket.

Other suitable fowl plants for the herb layer include: clover, buckwheat, wormwood, southernwood, chickweed, blackberry nightshade, amaranth, lucerne, cocksfoot, nettles, gotu kola and garlic. (The latter three plants have medicinal and tonic value for poultry, while wormwood helps repel fowl parasites. Multi-functionality is the go!)

Grains

If you have a really big backyard you might like to grow some grain for your birds.

Many grains are best utilised by poultry when fed in crushed or treated forms. However, there are some grains that are simple to grow and can be foraged freely. Wheat, buckwheat, barley, rye, triticale, corn, canola, maize and millet top the list. Sorghum is suitable if a low-tannin variety is used; sweet sorghum is ideal.

Millet varieties grown for bird seed are also good. White millet has the highest energy and protein of the millet family. A packet of bird seed can also produce a nice mixed forage crop.

Australia has its own millet – native panicum – from which Aboriginal people made protein-rich damper. Woollybutt is another native grain grass that grows on the outback plains. Exceptionally nutritious, the tiny seeds of woollybutt contain 13– 17% protein and large amounts of iron and zinc.

The use of native grasses for poultry forage would be well worth investigating. Drought-tolerant species could be particularly useful.

Quinoa is an excellent South American grain. Both the grain and the leaves of this plant are very nutritious. Quinoa is grown in Peru, Chile and Bolivia.

Vegetable protein seeds

If you don' t want to buy meat meal (an ingredient of layer pellets) for your birds, sourcing protein-rich vegetable feedstuffs can be a headache. By growing high-protein forage plants on site you can provide your own, saving time and money. You must be aware, however, of potential problems of toxicity that are common in high-protein crops.

Peas, beans and other such legumes are good sources of protein, but they are mostly deficient in the amino acids methionine, cystine and tryptophan. They also often have various toxic factors that must be destroyed by heat processing or sprouting. Amaranth has tiny nutritious seeds that contain a hepatoxic substance, so it must also be treated.

Soya beans, while an excellent source of all the amino acids, plus energy, should never be fed raw in poultry food because of the trypsin (enzyme) inhibitor, which makes digesting them difficult. Mung, lima and adzuki beans, on the other hand, are safe when raw and whole. Mung is an annual from Asia, with wild strains growing in Australia' s north. Sweet lupins are also useful, but beware of bitter strains which are highly toxic to birds.

Sunflowers contain about 15% protein and provide the equivalent energy of a cereal. The heads can either be cut and laid on the ground, dried and stored, or the seeds sprouted. They are an excellent source of linoleic acid and are a beautiful and easy plant to grow. Sesame seeds are also useful, being a good source of methionine and tryptophan, but are a poor source of lysine. They are best fed combined with soya beans, which are low in methionine.

Perennial nitrogen-fixing shrubs and trees, such as pigeon pea (in warm areas) and tagasaste (in temperate areas), provide excellent high-protein, ready-to-eat seeds. Australian wattles are also useful poultry forage plants. Black wattle is particularly appropriate due to its adaptation to rainforests, where soils are more nitrogen rich. It grows quite large and can become demanding of soil moisture and nutrients.

The summer seeds of the mirror bush are good, high-protein forage, as are the seeds of crotalaria, black locust, pea tree, and leucaena shrubs.

Pasture

Most grasses are useful for poultry greens if they are kept short, lush and palatable. When starting from scratch, try to select pasture species most favoured by poultry and matched to the climate and soil. Kikuyu and clovers are good, both are high in protein and make a good pasture combination. Lucerne, a tough long-lived perennial, is a valuable source of green pick and nutrients.

If you want to keep your lawn just for people, you could feed lawn mowings to birds. For this purpose, lawn is best cut with a hand mower and kept short.

Insect-attracting plants

In some parts of the world insects are recognised as a good source of protein and minerals in the human diet. Poultry, of course, relish them. Insects of all kinds will be attracted to a food forest, where poultry will prey upon them. In some areas Cadagi (tropical eucalpytus) trees attract beetles that poultry find delicious.

Weed awareness

It is recommended that you check the potential weed status of a plant before you introduce it to your garden system. Some plants can become pests in some areas, but not in others.

Endnotes

[1] Mollison, B. 1991, *Introduction to Permaculture*, Tagari, Australia.

Poultry Plant Profiles

Blackberry nightshade

Blackberry nightshade *(Solanum nigrum)* is a small herb that grows to about 1m in height. It is common throughout Australasia, Asia, America and the South Pacific, often appearing on disturbed land and in neglected garden corners.

Unlike the poisonous plants deadly nightshade *(Atropa belladonna)* – not found in Australasia – and green cestrun *(Cestrum parqui)* – which it resembles blackberry nightshade is quite safe to gro and eat. Many people traditionally cook the fruit, young leaves and shoots.

This hardy garden pioneer is usually dismissed as a useless or poisonous weec fact, quite the opposite is true. The succulent black berries are tiny taste treats, although, like other members of the Solanaceae family (such as tomatoes and potatoes), the green fruits contain the poisonous alkaloid solanine, so they must be eaten fully ripe. Animals never touch the green fruit.

Blackberry nightshade can be used to fill the semi-shady zones under the tree canopy of the food forest. It is not particular about soil types and, given sufficient water, it will produce copious quantities of vitamin-rich fruit. It will also self seed readily.

Blackberry nightshade

Black wattle

Black wattle *(Acacia melanoxylon)* provides good shade and protein-rich seeds. Unlike most wattles, it can tolerate high manure levels in the soil as it has adapted to life in lush rainforests.

In an orchard situation these trees grow too large and may not live for very long, especially if borers get the better of them. For these reasons this species could be a nuisance around fruit trees, where a smaller wattle would be better suited. Of course, you could use them as temporary 'nurse' trees, or keep them pruned back and turn the prunings into mulch or goat food. Japanese farming pioneer Fukuoka famously planted this Wattle in his orchards.

All wattle seeds have a hard seed coat and need either scarification or soaking in hot water in order to germinate.

Catnip

Catnip *(Nepeta cataria)*, which is also known as catmint, contains thymol and catnip oil, and can be used to repel lice. Its foliage also repels rodents and attracts cats.

A perennial member of the mint family, catnip tolerates frost and is grown from seed sown in spring, or from stem or root cuttings. The plant reaches 100cm in height and has small white flowers.

Catnip seems to live longer in cool climates with mild summers. Plant it in a sunny spot.

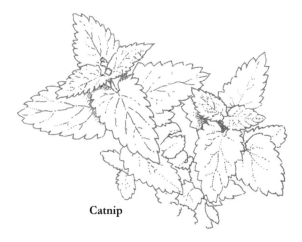

Catnip

Chickweed

Chickweed *(Stellaria media)* is a low, sprawling, cold-tolerant herb that likes moisture and shade. It is a common weed in Australia. A tropical version exists in warm areas.

A poultry favourite, chickweed has been used medicinally and as a human food for thousands of years. In Scandinavia, it is traditionally encouraged to grow in orchards as a good companion plant for trees.

Coastal wattle

This low-growing, sprawling wattle *(Acacia sophorae)* can be found growing along Australia's eastern and southern coastline. Fast growing, it was once a major food source for Aboriginal people, who ate the green pods steamed or roasted. The tiny seeds are high in protein.

To propagate the trees from seed, soak the seeds in hot water first or scarify them.

Comfrey

Comfrey *(Symphytum officinale)* is one of the best herbs to grow. It is a perennial herb which grows to 1.5m. It has branching hairy stems and leaves, an extensive fleshy root system, and its flowers are generally mauve.

A nutritious tonic food, comfrey is the only known vegetable source of vitamin B_{12}. Protein rich, comfrey also has medicinal properties. It's a cure for digestive disorders and, when pulverised in a blender, is used for poultices on wounds, sprains and broken bones. Allantoin is the active medicinal constituent.

Comfrey grows well where day and night are of equal length, so in tropical countries it will crop continuously throughout the year. In colder climates it may die down over winter and resprout in spring. Yields of over 100t of green forage to the acre in warm areas have been recorded. The protein yield from comfrey is said to be 20 times that from soya bean production.

Most of the comfrey plants in Australia are sterile hybrids and can only be propagated from root and crown cuttings. Comfrey grows rapidly with dressings of fresh poultry manure and lashings of water, becoming a good weed suppressor. It likes to grow in full sun in clean ground. After establishment (about a year) you can harvest leaves daily. If the plant is not pruned regularly the stems grow too coarse and must be mulched. Comfrey can keep up good production for 12 years before dying off. In cool climates it dies back each winter and is not so useful.

Fat hen

Fat hen *(Chenopodium album)* is a cosmopolitan weed that provided European peoples during the Iron Age with a staple food source from its seeds. It' s an annual herb, growing to 1m.

Closely related to fat hen is Good King Henry *(Chenopodium bonus-henricus)* – a perennial plant that grows to 60cm with large edible seeds and a thick fleshy root that was a popular food item in England up till 100 years ago.

Feverfew

This plant *(Tanacetum parthenium)* grows to 90cm and can be used like its relative pyrethrum, although it has only half the strength. A powder can be made from the pulverised dried, unopened flowers. It can also be made into a tea for spraying insects. It has medicinal uses too, for headache and fever. If sown after frost initially, feverfew will become frost hardy and grow easily, tolerating heat, poor soil, drought and weeds. The plant will re-seed readily.

Feverfew

Garlic

Garlic *(Allium sativum)* was once highly valued in Europe as a protection against the plague.

Garlic' s medicinal actions are many. The regular addition (weekly or monthly) of finely chopped garlic to food or water is a good worm preventative. Garlic stimulates digestive organs, relieves catarrh, regularises liver and gall bladder, treats intestinal infections and bacteria, and benefits blood circulation and heart action. It is also the supreme disinfectant.

Garlic

Garlic needs a sunny position to grow but is happy in poor soils. Plant the individual cloves 20cm apart and 5cm deep. Harvest 7 months later when the tops die down, leave them to dry in the sun for 2 or 3 days and store them in an airy, dry place. In cool climates you can plant them in spring and autumn, in hot climates only plant them in autumn.

Ginger

The aromatic root of ginger *(Zingiber officinalis)*, a native of tropical Asia, is an appetiser and stimulant. It helps relieve stomach problems and, as a hot ginger drink, eases cold symptoms and promotes perspiration. It is classified as an adjuvant, which means that it is a good additive to other herbal preparations. In China, ginger sprouts are used for de-worming people.

A piece of ginger root from the greengrocer' s can be left to shoot and then planted in a sunny, frost-free position.

Ginger root

Gotu kola
Gotu kola *(Centella asiatica),* also called swamp pennywort and the ' arthritis herb' , is a small-leafed, creeping plant of swampy places. It grows in southern Africa, Madagascar, India, Nepal and the western Pacific. Also found in the north and east coast of Australia, a similar looking species, *Centella cordifolia,* grows south of Nowra and across to Perth, but it does not have the same potency as the northern form.

According to Asian herbalists, gotu kola is one of the finest herb tonics, with rejuvenating effects on brain and body cells. They advise people to take several fresh leaves daily. Scientific analysis finds the herb to be a rich source of vitamins A, B, C, G, K, magnesium, asiatic and madecassic acids, plus the antibiotic asiaticoside. It also contains an oily, bitter tasting, volatile liquid called vellarin, and tannic acid.

Gotu kola has been used to treat a vast array of health problems for thousands of years. Currently, it is widely used in Europe (imported from Madagascar), where chemical extracts sell under various brand names. It is employed to treat people with diabetes, epilepsy, gangrene, burns, eczema, leprosy, wounds, ulcers, mental retardation, lupus, tuberculosis, gastric complaints and venous disorders. Gotu kola is also used for respiratory problems, nervous breakdown, venereal disease, impotence, menopause and cancer. Its action is anti-bacterial, anti-fungal and anti-aging. Many people chew a few leaves a day and report enhanced wellbeing, vitality and longevity. (Isobel Shepherd, ther Queeensland herbalist, recommends taking 5 or 5 leaves daily.)

Used externally, gotu kola is an excellent poultry remedy for skin conditions and fowl pox. It can be given internally as a general tonic.

Kangaroo apple

Kangaroo apple *(Solanum aviculare)* is a short-lived native ' bush tucker' shrub found growing from Victoria to Queensland, as well as in New Zealand and Papua New Guinea. The plant grows rapidly and provides light shade. After only 3 months it starts to produce the small juicy fruit relished by birds.

The Kangaroo apple tolerates a wide range of soil conditions (preferably well drained), torrential rain, drought, some frost and heat. As well as being hardy, it is a particularly ornamental plant suited for use as a screening plant. It self-seeds readily.

Seedlings are rarely harmed by foraging birds, because the leaves contain repellents. Because its leaves are rich in alkaloids, the plant is a commercially grown source of steroids and contraceptive hormones in Russia.

The fruit is abundant but variable to taste. Some people make chutney from sweet fruited varieties of this Solanum. However, there are toxic, bitter forms within the species, so it may be best to leave the berries to the birds.

Kangaroo apple

A word of warning: use kangaroo apple plant sparingly. Some of my birds appear to have been hormone affected. The hens have started to produce only female progeny and two warring tom turkeys, who started eating the fruit in a big way, decided to stop fighting and go sit on the nest together with their hens!

Lucerne
Lucerne *(Medicago sativa)*, also called alfalfa, is a valuable source of green pick and protein, providing vitamins A, D, K, and E, plus riboflavin, pantothenic and nicotinic acid. It is a tough perennial, lasting several years. Dried and chaffed lucerne can be fed to birds.

Mirror bush
This New Zealand plant *(Coprosma repens)* and other members of the genus are found growing wild along Australia's eastern coastline and in gardens. A common shrub, it has shiny leaves, with summer seeds good for poultry forage.

Nasturtium
This herb *(Tropaeolum majus)* is much appreciated by poultry. Richly medicinal, strongly antiseptic, a vermifuge (de-wormer) and appetiser (especially the seeds), nasturtium is also good for nervous ailments and depression, and it repels insect pests.

Nasturtium loves to grow in sandy soil in a sunny site and sprawls over fences and sheds. Clumping forms are also available. It is easy to grow from seed or cuttings. Preserve the seeds in vinegar and use them as a tonic and de-wormer.

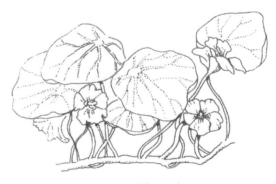

Nasturtium

Neem tree

A native of Burma and India, the neem tree *(Azedirachta indica)* is sacred in those places and known as the ' village pharmacy' . It is one of the most useful trees in the world. All parts of the tree have medicinal and insecticidal properties.

Rather than killing insects, Neem acts as a repellant and anti-feedent to them. In the USA several insect control products based on Neem are registered for use. It has enjoyed thousands of years of safe use in Asia.

Neem is a fast-growing tree, growing well even in poor soil and dry sites. It prefers a frost-free position, although more cold-tolerant highland species are available. Grow neem trees from seed.

Nettles

Stinging nettles *(Urtica* spp.*)* have long been used throughout Europe as a wild vegetable and were sold in markets in the 18th century. All English country cottage gardens once contained a nettle patch. They were also highly valued for maintaining livestock health.

Nettles are excellent for poultry as they promote good health, help to increase egg production and are very fattening. They are high in chlorophyll, iron, phosphorus, potassium, manganese, calcium, sulphur, silica, protein and vitamins A, C and D. Nettles are also a preventative against worms and contagion. A combination of powdered seaweed, comfrey and nettles is a powerful laying stimulant that, according to Juliette de Bairacli-Levy, can make even non-layers start to lay.[1]

When cut and withered, nettles lose the formic acid which gives them their sting. Dry and powder them finely, and add them to food. (This is good for humans, too!) You can also boil them for a few minutes to remove the sting and add them to cereal mash. Nettles boiled in whey are fed to combat worms in poultry.

Common/dwarf/lesser nettle *(U. urens)* is a European species which has naturalised throughout the world. It grows to 60cm in fertile, moist soil. A similar immigrant, tall nettle *(U. dioica)*, has hairier stems than the lesser nettle. The Australian native nettle (U. incisa) is found along creeks and in rainforests. It has been recorded that Aboriginal people baked this nettle species between hot stones.

Other uses recorded for this multi-purpose plant include the use of urtica oil derived from the seeds as lamp oil in Egypt. In Russia, boiled shoots are used to produce a beautiful permanent green dye for woollens, while roots boiled up in alum make a yellow dye to colour woollens and decorate eggs for Maundy Thursday.

When added to the compost heap, nettles are a great activator. They make great mulch, too. In addition, nettles are a good companion plant for aromatic herbs, mints and tomatoes. Biodynamic farmers use nettles in one of their compost preparations, known as 504.

You can make nettles into beer, a hair-restoring rinse and a tonic tea. You can also boil them in salt to make a vegetable rennet for cheese, or make linen from the mature stems. You can even make liquid fertiliser by soaking nettles in water for a couple of weeks, diluting to the colour of weak tea, straining and using. Always use nettles before the seeds ripen. The nettle is quite an amazing plant!

Oats
Oats *(Avena sativa)* can be made into a tonic drink –   just boil it up as you would for barley water. Sprouted oats provide many vitamins and minerals and are much more digestible than raw whole oats.

To sprout oats, soak them in warm water for a few hours, then wet them briefly on a daily basis. If the sprouts are kept in a piece of shadecloth or onion bag it makes them easy to dip in water. When the sprouts develop, spread them out and let them soak up some sunshine.

Pigeon pea
Pigeon pea *(Cajanus cajan)* is a legume shrub that provides one of the most important human food plants in India, a staple dahl dish made from the peas. The plant lives for around 9 years and grows to 3m, but ony in a frost-free environment.

A prolific seed bearer, the pigeon pea bears pods that must be shaken or hit to make them drop, otherwise parrots will eat the seeds. Direct seeding in late spring is best. Choose a sunny, well-drained location.

Pigweed

Pigweed *(Portulacca oleracea)* is a small, succulent annual creeping herb. It is a ' weed' found worldwide. Thriving in dryland areas, it has been part of the human diet for thousands of years, leaves being eaten either raw or steamed. In Australia, the tiny seeds were once a staple food for Aboriginal people. Portulacca is a a nutritious food rich in omega-3 fatty acids and antioxidants.

Rue

Rue *(Ruta graveolens)*, also called the ' herb of grace' , has both medicinal and insecticidal properties. Rue contains rutin, renowned for treating a host of diseases. Rue is used on the skin to remove parasites. It is a good wormer and is highly antiseptic. A border of rue is said to repel dogs, cats, wallabies and rabbits. Apply rue as a brew or a powder of dried leaves throughout feathers for lice. The herb is most potent when used fresh.

A small evergreen shrub, growing to 1m high, it is a hardy perennial that tolerates temperatures as low as -12°C. It prefers slightly alkaline soil and full sun. With its highly irritant leaves (full of rue oil), some people are allergic to rue and develop skin rashes. Treat the plant with care and use gloves when picking its leaves. Propagate rue by seed or division.

Southernwood

Southernwood *(Artemisia abrotanum)* is also known as lad' s love.

Southernwood is a powerful insect repellent and is used externally for lice in the form of a powder or brew rubbed through feathers. It is also a worm expeller, antiseptic and tonic. Medicinally, it is used for stomach problems and fever, for coughs, mucous congestion and bronchial catarrh. It is good to dry and strew on floors and is most powerful when leaves and flowers are picked just before opening. Fresh tops are used in weak brews.

Southernwood is an easily grown, perennial evergreen (although it may lose leaves in cold winter areas) that likes full sun and dry conditions. Plants can be divided or woody stem cuttings are taken in late winter or early spring.

Stinking Roger

Stinking Roger *(Tagetes minuta)* is usually regarded as a weed. A South American cousin of the marigold, it grows to 3m and smells strongly when brushed against. Its leaves are an irritant. Stinking Roger can be planted to deter flies, lice and mosquitoes. Fowl will eat the leaves. It can also be hung or strewn around as an insect repellant.

A good companion plant for tomatoes, the root exudates repel nematode and eelworm attacks on neighbouring plants. An old storage trick used by farmers at corn harvest time was to place a layer of stinking Roger plants between every three or four layers of corn cobs. This would repel weevils and even discourage rats.

Oddly enough, the ' stink' of this plant, said to be ' highly aromatic' , is due to essential oils which are commercially steam distilled in France and the United States. More pleasant when diluted, this Tagetes oil is used in the perfume industry, as well as for flavouring confectionery and desserts.

Flowers and leaves (flowers are strongest) can be steeped in a pan of boiling water with the lid on and let stand until cold. The brew can be mixed 1:1 with pyrethrum solution to spray around the fowl house. This annual plant can be established during any frost-free period. It grows easily from seed.

Tagasaste

For temperate, dry areas tagasaste *(Chamaecytisus palmensis)* is the ideal leguminous plant for the poultry yard. Known also as tree lucerne, tagasaste originates from the Canary Islands. Growing to 5 metres, this multi-purpose legume species provides fowl with shade, shelter, perches, year round green fodder, medicinal flowers in springtime (a great bird tonic) and large quantities of summer seed high in protein and carbohydrate.

Tagasaste is happy to grow in poor, sandy soils with low rainfall. It is slightly frost sensitive when young. While fairly adaptable to other soil and climate types, it does not handle waterlogging well. It can be planted closely in hedgerows with 0.5- 1m spacings, or in double rows of 1.5m spacings to make an excellent windbreak.

Tagasaste is regarded as a weed in parts of Western Australia.

Tansy

Another strewing herb, tansy *(Tanacetum vulgare)* is also a worming and medicinal herb. Its potassium-rich leaves are valuable compost activators and are used to repel mice, flies, fleas and ants.

Tansy grows to a height of up to 120cm. It tends to stay green over winter, and spreads by means of rhizome. Plants are easy to grow. In fact, they can become rampant. Divide them in spring or autumn. Harvest the leaves anytime.

Tansy

Wandering Jew

Wandering Jew *(Tradescantia albiflorra)* is a fleshy, creeping herb which often makes a pest of itself as it can become a rampant weed in gardens and rainforests. Poultry can be used to control infestations. The blue-flowered native variety can be used as edible salad vegetable for people as well.

Wandering Jew loves to grow in shady, moist situations, such as on creekbanks, where it can be harvested and rationed out for appreciative poultry of all ages.

White Cedar

Also known as Indian lilac, Persian Lilac and Pride of India/China, White Cedar *(Melia azederach)* is an Australasian rainforest tree that has similar qualities as the Neem tree. It is a popular street tree in inland areas. All parts of the tree are used traditionally, either as a medicine or an insecticide.

The leaves, flowers, root, bark or fruit are crushed and soaked in boiling water to cover. Leaves are insect and pest repellent, and are also used dried. The fruits are poisonous to pigs, sheep, goldfish and other species, but are devoured happily by pigeons and bats.

Wormwood

Wormwood *(Artemisia absinthium)* is an extremely bitter herb, used internally for all worms and externally as an insecticide.

An infusion of leaves is used as a wash for lice, and leaves are placed in cupboards to eradicate moths in clothes.

Wormwood is also an antiseptic, a stimulant, a nervine and mental restorer, a stomachic, an appetiser and a liver tonic. However, if too much is used internally it has the opposite effect and is poisonous.

The intensely bitter, tonic and stimulant qualities make it popular as an ingredient in liqueurs such as absinthe, which is made from absinthol, which is extracted from wormwood. Roman wormwood is an ingredient of Vermouth and it is also added to a special German wine that promotes appetite and digestion.

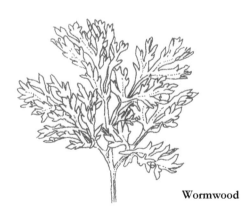

Wormwood

Wormwood can be planted in a sunny to shady situation. It is propagated by root division in spring or autumn, by cuttings, or with seeds sown in autumn, soon after ripening. Plant 600mm apart and keep weed free.

Wormwood gets straggly and benefits from pruning (you can make a hedge of it). It is drought resistant. It is an unsuitable companion for vegetables and many other plants, which will not prosper if they are grown close by, because of its hostile root exudates.

Like southernwood, wormwood is an easy-to-grow, evergreen perennial, although it may lose its leaves in cold winter areas. It is a good herb to dry and strew on floors and is most powerful when leaves and flowers are picked just before opening. Fresh tops are used in weak brews.

Endnote
[1]   Bairacli Levy, Juliette de 1976, *Herbal Handbook for Farm and Stable*, Rodale Press, United States of America.

Backyard Poultry Produce

Having fresh fried eggs for breakfast may be your sole reason for keeping birds in the backyard. But are you aware of the other uses for eggs and poultry produce? Some traditional Asian medicines are made from eggs, while eggs and feathers make popular craft items. Poultry manure is another valuable output.

Excellent eggs

Eating eggs

The campaign to reduce heart disease in Australia has much maligned the egg as a non-'heart-smart' food, making it somewhat unfashionable. But lately the demonisation of cholestrol, that eggs are rich in, has been discovered to be on shakey ground. Cholestrol is actually good for you!

Eggs are great food, but a sensible approach would be to put them into the context of one's diet and lifestyle. Sure, a couple of greasy fried eggs on toast, with a big slab of butter may not be too healthy. But if you don't eat meat, it might be ok.

The egg is really a wholesome package of goodness. (Don't think that shell colour has anything to do with it, though.) The average egg is made up of:
- 7.2g protein
- 0.6g carbohydrate
- 6.7g fat
- 41g water.

The white contains virtually no fat, and the fat in the yolk is in a saturated form. Eggs are also a valuable source of iron; vitamins A, D and B; riboflavin; niacin and thiamine. The amount each egg contains depends on the variety in the hen's diet. (Eggs are most nutritious when eaten raw.)

If you grow a few potatoes and green vegetables, and keep hens in your backyard, you can enjoy balanced, wholesome meals that you have produced all yourself. Now that brings satisfaction!

As for duck eggs, they are the most widely eaten eggs in the world. They are used in exactly the same way as fowl eggs. Some people find the flavour of duck eggs a little too strong. If you find them too flavoursome, you can always use them in cooking – bake a cake, whip up a Spanish omelette... there are plenty of egg recipes to choose from.

Collecting, storing and cooking eggs

There is an art to collecting eggs for eating, if you want to enjoy them at their best. Because eggs rapidly deteriorate when warm, you should gather them when they are as fresh as possible. As long as they are refrigerated, eggs will keep well for many weeks, although they will soon dry out if kept in the egg rack and are best kept in a carton if they are not going to be used straight away.

It is best to keep nests as clean as possible so that eggs are also kept clean. If eggs are dirty, try to keep their protective outer membrane intact, by not soaking or wetting them. Eggshells are quite porous so if the membrane is washed off, the egg is more easily contaminated. A brisk rub with a rough mitt or a rag that is only just damp will usually do the trick.

Occasionally a mystery egg will turn up in an overlooked spot and you'll wonder whether it is fresh or stale. A classic test is to dunk the egg in a bowl of cool water and see if it sinks, in which case it is fresh. An old, stale egg is very gaseous and will float to the top.

Another test for freshness is to break an egg into a pan to see how firm the white and yolk are. If the white stands up high around the yolk and doesn't spread all over the pan, then it is fresh. This firm structure breaks down with heat and aging. If the egg is kept at 20°C it will only stay fresh for 2 weeks. You could write the date on one end of each egg, in pencil, just to be sure.

When it is time to eat the eggs, let them first warm up to room temperature after their stint in the fridge. Use the freshest eggs for frying. If the eggs are to be boiled, however, select eggs that are a few days old as they will be easier to shell. Never over-boil eggs: they become tough and indigestible. A light simmer will do.

Decorating eggs

Eggs have long been used as symbols of new life, especially in springtime. They were also taken up as a Christian symbol at Eastertime, that is, until the chocolate egg took over!

A colourful tradition of many cultures is to dye and decorate eggs, whether raw, boiled or blown (empty). The coloured eggs are then hung as mobiles, hung on Christmas trees or displayed in special egg stands. Acrylic paints or traditional herb dyes can be used and the egg varnished afterwards.

To dye eggs naturally, soak them in any of the following herbal brews to obtain a variety of colours:
- onion skins, boiled – brown, red or purple dye
- beetroot – soft red brown
- comfrey leaves – yellow
- elder berries – lavender
- parsley leaves – light green
- tansy flowers – yellow
- mulberries – a mulberry red
- spinach leaves – a light green
- nettle roots, boiled in alum – yellow.

To create a special effect you can drop hot wax onto the eggs before soaking them in cold-water dyes. The wax resists the dye and can be scraped off afterwards.

Ukrainian Easter eggs, known as ' pysanky' , are intricately patterned symbols of life, love and friendship. Patterns are first drawn on the egg in pencil. Then, hot wax is applied using a kistka, which resembles an Indonesian batik tool used to apply wax to cloth before dying. The eggs are then dyed with commercial egg dyes. An egg can be dyed up to five times this way. More wax is added each time, but is only removed at the

A decorated egg, Faberge style.

end. The wax is warmed near a flame and then wiped off with a soft cloth.

A more elaborate method of egg decorating is the Faberge style, which is based on the creations of a French jeweler. This style is very ornate and incorporates gold and silver trim, carving and miniature scenes. Large, strong-shelled eggs are needed for this style - the bigger eggs of ducks and geese are more frequently used than fowl eggs.

Fabulous feathers

Ancient peoples the world over have marveled at the beauty of feathers. Some ancient peoples have ascribed mystical qualities to feathers, but it is mainly their ornamentality that appeals. Elegant ostrich plumes and peacock tail feathers have been enormously popular in modern times.

New Zealand Maori tradition holds feathers in high regard, using them to decorate hair as well as cloaks, canoes, baskets and sacred objects. Beautifully carved family treasure boxes were used to hold such valuable items as feathers from rare birds. Kites made from flax had feathers attached to the nose and tail for improved aerodynamic qualities. A feather cloak was the most highly prized family heirloom, especially if made from the feathers of albino kiwi birds.

American Indians adorn their headdresses with colourful turkey feathers and also create other traditional craft work with feathers. Mandalas (decorative circular symbols of spiritual significance) and circular hanging ' dream-catchers' are typically adorned with feathers.

Hats, head bands, costumes, jewelry, mobiles, pens, arrows and totem poles can be decorated with feathers. Add feathers to dried flower arrangements and indoor pot plants. People fishing for bass use feathers tied on lures. Barred Plymouth Rock and Wyandotte rooster hackle feathers are favoured for this purpose.

Naturally shed feathers can be collected around moulting time. Messy or tattered feathers can go on the compost heap – they are an excellent source of nitrogen. The smaller, downy feathers from culled birds can be used to stuff a pillow, quilt or mattress. (The commercial items from Asia are generally made by harvesting down from *live* geese.)

When collecting down feathers, it is best to dry pluck, as washing can make feathers mat together. You can lightly wash the feathers in warm soapy water. Bag them in an old pillowcase initially, then spread them thinly over something like shadecloth to dry.

A word of warning: feathers are biodegradable. Tiny mites will eventually feast on them, so you may need to occasionally spray them with a safe insecticide, such as pyrethrum.

Feathers have long been favoured for hat decoration.

Magnificent manure

Poultry manure can be a great asset to a gardener, but if it is unused and allowed to leach into the soil it can pollute groundwater and streams, and contribute to toxic algal blooms.

Manure changes the natural nutrient status of soil, making it hostile to many plants. Fowl manure is rich in phosphorus and many Australian plants detest phosphorus. Like all manure, it needs to be responsibly managed.

Poultry manure has one of the highest fertiliser values of all the livestock manures. As it comes combined with urine (the white part of the dropping), it is made up of:
- 1.63% nitrogen
- 1.54% phosphoric acid
- 0.85% potassium.

Compare this with fresh cattle manure, which is:
- 0.29% nitrogen
- 0.17% phosphoric acid
- 0.10% potassium.

Poultry manure is also a rich source of calcium, copper and other trace elements.

This manure can make an excellent plant food, but is too strong to be directly applied to most plants and needs to be diluted or broken down for best results.

Use it to make an excellent liquid fertiliser for garden and crops.

Soak fresh manure in water, at about 1 part manure to 10 parts water. Keep a lid on the container as the mixture really smells. After a week or so, dilute the mixture down (1:10 again), until it is golden in colour, not dark. Only then will it be safe to water plants with. Even so, it is best to apply the liquid fertiliser to wet soil and not on to leaves.

Making compost

Because the potassium in manure can quickly leach out in water and ammonia outgasses from it, manure must be used quickly, or else kept in a covered heap. A good solution is to make it into compost, which, if properly made, will be the best plant fertiliser and soil restorer you could ever use.

To make compost, place sawdust or straw under fowl perches or around duck houses and wait until there is a good pile of droppings. (A large hen can annually produce 55kg of manure.) Meanwhile, gather stockpiles of organic materials such as weeds, leaves and food scraps. Build the compost heap by spreading these materials in layers. Find a spot where the largest possible heap can fit and be turned. The bigger the compost heap, the better.

Bacteria in the heap, which break down organic materials, prefer an optimum carbon to nitrogen ratio of about 20– 30 to 1. Carbon is supplied by dry or old plant materials such as rice hulls or wood shavings. Nitrogen is abundant in manures, fresh greens, blood and bone, and bonemeal.

Keep layers of nitrogen-rich materials thin, sandwiching them between thicker carbon-rich layers.

Saturate each layer with water, aiming for about 50% moisture. Sprinkle each layer with a fine dusting of lime or wood ash to reduce acidity and aid decomposition. Cover the finished heap with a thatching of straw, grass or soil, to shed rain and keep moisture and nutrients in.

Microorganisms will soon start breaking down the heap. You' ll know they are working when the heap becomes hot, reaching temperatures of up to 60°C!

After about 2 weeks it will be time to turn the heap over and wet any dry spots. If all goes well, in another week or two it should smell sweet and be ready for use.

Keep a little of the finished compost as a bacterial starter that can be sprinkled between the layers of your next compost heap.

Using compost

Compost can be spread around trees, vegetables, indoor plants and the like. Apply about 1kg of compost per square metre of soil. Dig it in a bit and cover it over with mulch to protect it from the elements.

Now the soil will be greatly improved, becoming soft, friable and full of life. The wonderful health and vigour of plants grown with compost helps to protect them from diseases and pests. Crops will taste delicious, too.

Compost worms

Some people feed their half-rotted compost (not too fresh or hot) to special compost worms. These are similar to earthworms, except they only eat rotting vegetable material. The worms can also be fed to poultry; they make an excellent high-protein meal.

Known as tiger and red worms, the compost worms grow fat and breed quickly when fed on compost and kept cool and moist in their boxes. The worm castings they produce are rich in easily assimilated nutrients that are perfect for plants.

Worm farming is becoming popular. At a minimum, all you need is a foam box lined with semi-composted material and a piece of hessian material to cover it. Regularly top it up with chopped up kitchen scraps, horse or cow manure, or semi-composted poultry manure (not fresh manure). All things wet and mushy will be enjoyed by worms. Wet, shredded newspaper and the odd sprinkle of lime is also popular with them.

By turning poultry manure into food – fruit, vegetables and worms – you save money and prevent environmental degradation.

It's a beautiful closed-circuit system!

Botanical names of plants

Adzuki bean	*Phaseolus angularis*
Alder, English	*Alnus glutinosa*
Amaranth	*Amaranthus hypochondriacus*
Angelica	*Angelica archangelica*
Aniseed/Anise	*Pimpinella anisum*
Apple berry	*Billardiera scandens*
Apple	*Malus domestica*
Arrowroot	*Canna edulis*
Bamboo	*Bambusa* spp., *Arundinaria* spp., *Phyllostachys* spp.
Banana passionfruit	*Passiflora mollissima*
Barley	*Hordeum* spp.
Bilberry	*Vaccinium myrtillus*
Black gram bean	*Phaseolus mungo*
Black locust	*Robinia pseudoacacia*
Blackberry nightshade	*Solanum nigrum*
Blackwood wattle	*Acacia melanoxylon*
Bramble	*Rubus fructuosus* (Blackberry), *R. parvifolius* (Native)
Buckwheat	*Fagopyrum esculentum*
Burdekin plum	*Pleiogynium timorense*
Cabbage	*Brassica oleracea*
Cadagi tree	*Eucalyptus torrelliana*
Camphor laurel tree	*Cinnamomum camphora*
Canola/Rape	*Brassica napus*
Carrot	Daucus carota
Cassava (root)	*Manihot esculenta* (bitter cassava), *M. dulcis* (sweet cassava)

Catechu	*Catechu nigrum*
Catnip/Catmint	*Nepeta cataria*
Cayenne pepper	*Capsicum frutescens*
Cedar	*Cedrus* spp.
Celery	*Apium graveolens* var. *rapaceum*
Chamomile, English	*Chamaemelum nobile*
Chamomile, German	*Matricaria recutita*
Chard	*Beta vulgaris* var. *cicla*
Chickweed	*Stellaria media*
Chilean cestrum/Green cestrum	*Cestrum parqui*
Chilli	*Capsicum frutescens*
Chives	*Allium schoenoprasum*
Choko	*Sechium edule*
Chou moellier	*Brassica oleracea*
Citronella	*Cymbopogon nardus*
Cleavers	*Galium aperine*
Clover	*Trifolium* spp.
Coastal wattle	*Acacia sophorae*
Cocksfoot	*Dactylis glomerata*
Columbine	*Aquilegia vulgaris*
Comfrey	*Symphytum officinale*
Cotoneaster	*Cotoneaster glaucophyllus, C. pannosus*
Cotton lavender	*Santolina chamaecyparissus*
Crab apple	*Malus* spp.
Cress	*Barbarea verna*
Crotalaria	*Crotalaria spectabilis*
Cucumber	*Cucumis sativus*
Dandelion	*Taraxacum officinale*
Davidson' s plum	*Davidsonia pruriens*
Deadly nightshade	*Atropa belladonna*
Dill	*Anethum graveolens*
Elder, black	*Sambucus nigra*
Endive	*Cichorium endivia*
Eucalyptus	*Eucalyptus* spp.
European buttercup	*Ranunculus* spp.

Fat hen	*Chenopodium album*
Fennel	*Foeniculum vulgare*
Fenugreek	*Trigonella foenum-graecum*
Feverfew	*Tanacetum parthenium*
Fig, native	*Ficus* spp.
Garlic	*Allium sativum*
Gentian	*Gentiana lutea*
Geranium	*Pelargonium spp.*
Ginger	*Zingiber officinalis*
Goat's rue	*Galega officinalis*
Good King Henry	*Chenopodium bonus-henricus*
Gooseberries	*Ribes uva-crispa*
Gotu kola/Swamp pennywort	*Centella asiatica*
Grape	*Vitis vinifera*
Groundsel	*Senecio vulgaris*
Hemlock	*Conium maculatum*
Hemp	*Cannabis sativa*
Horseradish	*Armoracia rusticana*
Hyssop	*Hyssopus officinalis*
Inkweed/Pokeroot	*Phytolacca decandra, P. americana*
Jerusalem artichoke	*Helianthus tuberosus*
Juniper	*Juniperus communis*
Kamala	*Mallotus philippensis*
Kangaroo apple	*Solanum aviculare*
Kikuyu	*Pennisetum clandestinum*
King Island melilot	*Meliotus indicus*
Kudzu	*Pucraria thunbergiana*
Lamb's lettuce	*Valerianella locusta*
Larkspur	*Consolida ambigua*
Lavender	*Lavendula* spp.
Leek	*Allium paniculatum*
Lemon grass	*Cymbopogon ambiguus*

Leucaena	*Leucaena leucocephala*
Licorice	*Glycyrrhiza glabra*
Lilly pilly	*Acmena smithii*
Lily of the valley	*Convallaria majalis*
Lima bean	*Phaseolus lunatus*
Linseed	*Linum usitatissimum*
Lucerne/Alfalfa	*Medicago sativa*
Maise/Corn	*Zea mays*
Male fern	*Dryopteris filix-mas*
Marigold/Calendula	*Calendula officinalis*
Marjoram	*Origanum majorana*
Mat rush	*Lomandra* spp.
Melaleuca	*Melaleuca* spp.
Millet	*Panicum* spp.
Mirror bush	*Coprosma repens*
Molucca bramble	*Rubus moluccanus*
Mother of millions	*Kalanchoe tubiflora*
Mugwort	*Artemesia vulgaris*
Mulberry	*Morus rubra, M. nigra, M. alba*
Mulberry, native	*Hedycarya angustifolia*
Mullein	*Verbascum thapsus*
Mung bean	*Vigna radiata*
Mustard	*Brassica juncea*
Nasturtium	*Tropaeolum majus*
Neem tree	*Azadirachta indica*
Nettle	*Urtica dioca, U. incisa, U. urens*
Oats	*Avena sativa*
Onion	*Allium cepa*
Oregon	*Pseudotsuga menziesii*
Oxalis	*Oxalis* spp.
Pacific coral tree	*Erythrina variegata*
Paprika	*Capsicum annum*
Parsley	*Petroselinum cripsum*
Parsnip	*Pastinaca sativa*

Pasque flower	*Pulsatilla vulgaris*
Passionfruit	*Passiflora edulis*
Pawpaw/papaya	*Carica papaya*
Pea tree	*Caragana arborescens, C. siberica*
Pea	*Pisum sativum*
Pear	*Pyrus communis*
Pennyroyal	*Mentha pulegium*
Pepper	*Piper nigrum*
Peppermint	*Mentha* x *piperita*
Persimmon	*Diospyros kaki*
Petty spurge	*Euphorbia peplus*
Pigeon pea	*Cajanus cajan*
Pigweed	*Portulacca oleracea*
Plantain	*Plantago major*
Potato	*Solanum tuberosum*
Pumpkin	*Cucurbita maxima*
Pyrethrum	*Tanacetum cinerariifolium*
Quassia chips (wood chips of)	*Quassia amara*
Quinoa	*Chenopodium quinoa*
Rhubarb	*Rheum rhabarbarum*
Rice	*Oryza vesicaria* subsp. *sativa*
Rocket	*Eruca vesicaria* subsp. *sativa*
Rosemary	*Rosmarinus officinalis*
Rue	*Ruta graveolens*
Rye	*Secale cereale*
Safflower	*Carthamus tinctorius*
Sage	*Salvia officinalis*
Salsify	*Tragopogon porrifolius*
Sassafras	*Doryphora sassafras*
Senna	*Cassia senna*
Sesame	*Sesamum indicum*
Shepherd's purse	*Capsella bursa-pastoris*
Silverbeet	*Beta vulgaris* var. *cicla*
Slippery elm	*Ulmus rubram* syn *U. fulva*
Sorghum	*Sorghum bicolor*
Southernwood	*Artemisia abrotanum*

Sow thistle	*Sonchus oleraceus*
Soya bean	*Glycine max*
Spearmint	*Mentha spicata viridus*
Spurry	*Spergula arvensis* (corn spurry),
	Spergularia rubra (sand spurry)
St John's Wort	*Hypericum perforatum*
Stinking Roger	*Tagetes minuta*
Sunflower	*Helianthus annuus*
Sweet lupins	*Lupinus* spp.
Sweet potato	*Ipomoea batata*
Tagasaste	*Chamaecytisus palmensis*
Tansy	*Tanacetum vulgare*
Tea-tree	*Leptospermum* spp., *Melaleuca* spp.
Thistle, varigated	*Silybum marianum*
Thyme	*Thymus vulgaris*
Triticale	*Triticum aestivum* x *Secale cereale*
Turnip	*Brassica rapa* var. *septiceps*
Vervain	*Verbena officinalis*
Vetch	*Vicia sativa*
Virginia creeper	*Parthenocissus quinquefolia*
Wandering Jew	*Tradescantia albiflora*
Wheat (grain of)	*Triticum aestivum*
White cedar	*Melia azedarach*
Woollybut	*Eucaluptus delegatensis*
Wormwood	*Artemisia absinthium*

References

Agriculture and Resource Management Council of Australia and New Zealand, Animal Health Committee, 1995, *Australian Model Code of Practice for the Welfare of Animals, Domestic Poultry,* 3rd edition, Australia.

Animal Liberation, n.d. *Battery Hens* (leaflet), Animal Liberation, Australia.

Animal Liberation, n.d. *Broiler Chickens* (leaflet), Animal Liberation, Australia.

Bairacli Levy, Juliette de 1976, *Herbal Handbook for Farm and Stable,* Rodale Press, United States of America.

Burton, H.W. 1992, ' Ducklings Can Drink Themselves to Death' *Australasian Poultry,* June- July, vol. 3, no. 2, p. 28.

' Cautious welcome for draft European livestock standards' *New Farmer and Grower,* Nov. 1996, Joy Michaud (ed). Soil Association, United Kingdom.

Cobbitt, W. 1822, *Cottage Economy,* Oxford University Press, New York.

Cribb, A.B. & J.W. 1987, *Wild Food in Australia,* 2nd edn, Fontana/ Collins, Sydney, New South Wales.

Cumming, Prof. R. 1991 ' Can Coccidiosis be Controlled by Nutrition?' , *Australasian Poultry,* Dec., vol. 2, no. 5, p. 8.

Davis, K. 1996, *Prisoned Chickens, Poisoned Eggs: an inside look at the modern poultry industry,* Phd Book Publishing Company, United States of America.

Evans, M., *Nutrient Composition of Feedstuffs for Pigs and Poultry,* Department of Primary Industries, Queensland.

Fair, W.C. 1930, *People' s Home Stock Book,* Oceanic Publishing Company, Ohio, Cleveland.

Fanton, J. & Fanton, M. 1996 ' KRRS vs KFC' , *The Seed Savers' Network Newsletter*, no. 20, Autumn, p. 6.

Fernando, Dr S. 1982, *Traditional Herbal Food and Medicines in Sri Lanka,* FAO, Sri Lanka.

Fitzgerald, M. 1991, ' Basic Chookery' , *GrassRoots*, no. 84, pp. 27- 28.

Fritz, S., & Andresen, T. 1994, *Organic Animal Husbandry,* Fritz and Associates, Australia.

Grieves, Mrs 1931, *A Modern Herbal,* Tiger Books, United Kingdom.

Healy, P. 1988, ' Poultry the Organic Way' , *Growing Today*, Spring, p. 3.

Hills, L.D. 1974, *The Comfrey Report,* Henry Doubleday Research Association, United Kingdom.

Hunter, F. 1988, *Homoeopathic First Aid Treatment for Pets,* Thorsens Books, Great Britain.

James, Dr. T. 1994, ' Scaly Leg in Poultry' , *Australasian Poultry*, April- May, vol. 5, no. 1, p. 28.

Kohl, M.F. & Gainer, C. 1991, *Good Earth Art,* Bright Ring Publishing, United States of America.

Lamp, C. & Collet, F. 1976, *A Field Guide to Weeds in Australia,* Inkata Press, Australia.

Low, T. 1985, *Wild Herbs of Australia,* Angus and Robertson, Australia.

Low, T. 1989, *Bush Tucker,* Angus and Robertson, Australia.

Mark, P. 1997, ' Freedom Beckons' , *Action*, no. 59, Sept., pp. 6- 7.

Marold, L. 1995, *Chookwise*, L. Marold, Castlemaine. Distributed by Marold-Hof, PO Box 54, Castlemaine Vic 3450 Australia.

Miller, M. (comp.) 1996, *Rare and Minority Breeds of Poultry in Australia*, Australian Rare and Minority Breeds Association Inc., Elphinstone, Victoria.

Miller, M. & Riley, J. 1989, *Poultry Breeders Directory*, Night Owl Publishers, Shepparton, Victora.

Mollison, Bill, 1991, *Introduction to Permaculture*, Tagari, Australia.

Pereira, J.P. 1989, ' Pesticide Properties of White Cedar' , *International Permaculture Journal*, Issue 31, Permaculture International, Lismore, New South Wales.

Singer, Prof. P. 1977, *Animal Liberation*, Paladin/Granada Publishing, Great Britain.

Woodrow, L. 1996, *The Permaculture Home Garden*, Viking/Penguin Books, Australia.

Glossary

Aconite: a tincture made from monkshood *(Aconitum napellus)* and used to treat, among other things, cases of shock or fright, accidents or injuries, as well as acute fever or influenza, burns and bleeding.

allopathic health system: the ' modern' system of medicine, based on synthetic chemical remedies.

Arnica: a homeopathic remedy made from the small daisy leopard' s bane *(Arnica montana)*. Arnica is used to treat a number of conditions, including shock, haemorrhage, bruising, fractures, strains, bites, fright, trauma and limb paralysis.

Arsenicum: a poison which, when used as a homeopathic remedy, counteracts acute vomiting and diarrhoea, as well as some chronic skin conditions.

auto-sexing: refers to breeds of fowl that have ' -bar' on the ends of their names, that can be sexed at hatching according to the colour of their down.

bantam: the small version of any breed of domestic fowl. Most poultry breeds have a small-sized counterpart. True bantams have no large counterpart.

-bar: this suffix is used to denote the auto-sexing breeds.

battery farming: the commercial process of keeping laying hens in small cages within a large, controlled environment

biodynamic agriculture: a system of agriculture developed from the teachings of Rudolf Steiner. It emphasises soil health using organic methods.

botulism: a disease of the nervous system caused by eating spoiled food, or food containing the organism *Clostridium botulinum*. Causes neck paralysis and death.

broiler: fowl bred for rapid development and large growth in the shortest time period, specifically raised for meat.

broody: the term used to describe birds desiring to sit on a clutch of eggs.

brooder box: a box used for raising little chickens without a mother, providing warmth and feed.

chamomilla: a homeopathic remedy made from the wild chamomile plant *(Matricarra chamomilla)* and used to treat pain.

chick: Fowl in their first few weeks; the young of the domestic fowl.

clucky: like ' broody' , this term describes birds desiring to sit on a clutch of eggs

clutch: a setting of eggs. Also, a brood of chickens.

Coccidiosis: an infectious disease that is caused by protozoan parasites that attack the intestines, generally of young birds. Rarely encountered in a clean, natural environment where birds are uncrowded.

coccidiostat: an additive to proprietary food to protect young fowl from coccidiosis. Poisonous to ducks and unnecessary for older fowl.

cock: a male fowl.

cockerel: a young male domestic fowl; before maturity.

comb: fleshy growth on the heads of domestic fowl, usually larger on male birds. Each breed has a distinctive style of comb.

crop: a pouch-like enlargement of a fowl' s gullet, which is used to hold food before it passes to the gizzard for initial grinding prior to digestion.

cropbound: a condition in which long fibres get tangled and stick in the crop.

crossbred: describes a bird produced by crossbreeding, not a purebred.

crumbles: a feed mix for chickens with particles small enough for their consumption.

debeaking: the practice of removing part of a fowl' s beak. It counteracts feather picking and cannibalism in fowl in overcrowded conditions, but inflicts pain and suffering.

deep litter: a thick layer of straw or sawdust. Birds in permanent pens are usually provided with deep litter in which to scratch. Should be regularly topped up, replaced regularly, and composted.

derris dust: a natural remedy made from any plant of the genus Derris, the roots of which contain rotenone. Used to repel mites and lice. Hazardous to fish.

drake: a male duck.

drakeling: a young male duck.

duck: wild or domesticated web-footed swimming birds of the genus *Anas,* characterised by a broad, flat bill and short legs. Also the female of this bird.

dustbath: a shallow excavation in the topsoil in which fowl will lie and roll as a natural means of controlling lice and mites.

ecosystem: a community of inter-related organisms and their environment, where there is a natural balance of plant and animal species.

egg bound: unable to lay an egg, usually because of a blockage of the reproductory tract.

feathering up: describes the process during which downy chicks gain their true feathering.

flighty: a term used to describe breeds that are nervous and excitable.

forage: the act of searching for provisions (seeds, insects, fruits and greens) in a natural environment.

fowl: the domesticated hen or cock, as distinct from ducks, geese, turkeys etc; a bird descended from wild species of Jungle Fowl *(Gallus)*.

fowl pox: a viral condition causing lessions/scabs on the face of fowl. Mainly spread by mosquitoes.

free-range: a fowl management system involving ranging fowls over extensive areas during the day.

Gelsemium: a homeopathic remedy made from wild jasmine *(Gelsemium sempervirens)* used to treat fright, fever and influenza etc.

green pick: vegetative forage foods.

heavy breed: large, slow moving, heavily feathered breeds, mainly of Asian origin, that are generally bred for meat production.

hen: mature female domestic fowl.

hen feathering: describes breeds in which the cock has the same feather patterning as the hen.

homeopathic medicine: a system of medicine based mainly on herbal remedies that are given in an extremely diluted form on the basis that ' like cures like' .

hybrid: offspring produced by crossing different breeds of purebred fowl.

Hypericum: a tincture made from the herb St John' s wort *(Hypericum perforatum)* and used to treat pain.

Ignatia: a homeopathic remedy used to treat grief.

incubate: to hatch eggs, either by the hen sitting on them or by providing artificial heat.

incubator: a machine used to incubate eggs artificially.

layer fatigue: exhaustion caused by overproduction of eggs. A condition which affects commercial layers.

light breed: a slim breed selected for egg-laying ability. Light breeds have less feathering than heavy breeds, are more active foragers, and tend to be more flighty.

Marek's disease: a viral condition related to the herpes virus which causes paralysis, tumours, and high mortality. Spread by feather particles in dust. Some breeds of fowl are more resistant to the disease than others. The disease can be vaccinated against, although this may not be 100% effective.

microorganisms: naturally occurring bacteria that feeds on organic matter.

monoculture: single-product manufacturing.

moult: the annual loss and replacement of birds' feathers.

muffs: thick feathering around the ears and neck; ' muffling' .

Nux Vomica: a homeopathic remedy made from the seeds of the poison-nut tree *(Srychnos nux vomica)*, which is used to treat a range of conditions including chronic colic, digestive upsets and loss of appetite.

parasite: an animal that lives in or on poultry, obtaining nutrients from the body it inhabits. Causes discomfort or disease.

permaculture: permanent agriculture. A food production system that integrates plant and animal crops and which fosters sustainability and biodiversity as part of its design.

point-of-lay: a pullet that is almost ready to start laying eggs; about 6 months old.

poultry: domesticated birds –   fowl, ducks, turkeys, guinea fowl, geese.

pullet: a young hen under 12 months of age.

Pulsatilla: a homeopathic remedy made from the pasque flower *(Anemone pulsatilla)* and used to treat depression.

purebred: an animal that has been selectively bred until certain features are ' fixed' and its type will breed true.

rescue remedy: a combination of homeopathic remedies in one. Specifically for shock and distress.

rooster: mature male of the domestic fowl; cock.

rotenone: the active ingredient in derris dust, a safe insecticide.

salmonella: a group of bacterial families that cause food poisoning.

caly leg: a disease caused by a small mite that bores through the scales
f the leg and forms deposits, forcing the scales outwards.

cutellaria: made from the herb scullcap *(Scutellaria lateriflora)*. It is a
omeopathic remedy used to treat nervous temperaments and
onditions.

etting: a collection of eggs for hatching.

exing: the act of determining which birds are male and which are
male.

andard breed: refers to the size, as opposed to bantam.

actoring: the use of poultry to work over ground that needs clearing in
reparation for growing crops.

ent: the excretory opening of a bird. Also, the opening through which
gs are layed.

attles: fleshy appendages hanging down from the throat and chin of
me fowl breeds.

Index

Photography credits

Unless otherwise specified, all photographs are by
Alanna Moore and Scott Buckingham.
Photos on pages 14 and 48 are courtesy of Rosalie Franklin.
Breed photographs no.s 24 - 44 are by Josh Bradley.
Breed photograph no. 13 is by Peter Still.
Breed photograph no. 2 is by Linda Marold.
Breed photographs no.s 1, 3, 4, 5, 6, 7, 8, 10, 11, 12, 14, 17, 18, 20, 21 are by Andy Vardy.

 PYTHON PRESS

Publishing books on eco-living,
permaculture, natural building,
dowsing and geomancy
since 2001.

See **www.pythonpress.com**

or send a self addressed envelope to
Python Press
PO Box 929 Castlemaine Vic 3450 Australia.

Printed in the USA
CPSIA information can be obtained
at www.ICGtesting.com
LVHW072100170224
772034LV00006B/103

9 780975 778289